A STUDY OF THE SHORT STORY

BY

HENRY SEIDEL CANBY, PH.D.
Assistant Professor of English in the Sheffield Scientific School of Yale University

NEW YORK
HENRY HOLT AND COMPANY

THE QUINN & BODEN CO. PRESS
RAHWAY, N. J.

PREFACE

In this book I have tried to present a brief, clear, and reasonably comprehensive account of the short story in English and American literature. I have tried to characterize faithfully the broader movements, selecting from the vast literature of short narrative the writing which has been vital either in itself or because of its influence.

Wider reference to short-story literature, and full bibliographical details, will be found in *The Short Story in English* (Henry Holt and Company, 1909). With that book as background, it seemed possible to write a simpler, less detailed account of short-story history, for the use of college classes, and for such readers as might combine a desire for brevity with their interest in the short story. The two books are complementary. The historical development of the short story is discussed in both; for a "documented" investigation, and for the basis of many generalizations, the reader should go to the earlier and larger work.

Nevertheless, although I have taken advantage of the information accessible in *The Short Story in English* to free the following pages from hindering bibliography and frequent reference to minor literature, I have done all possible to make this new history of the short story more discriminating, more just, and more true. The historical periods and the course of development laid down before have been verified by later study, but I have felt as free to modify the critical conclusions of my earlier work as to borrow from them.

To this brief history have been added eleven illustrative stories, for the convenience of classes and the general reader. These are not the "eleven best stories"; the list is not even as completely representative as I could wish of the best American and English short-story writers. Closely held copyrights would make an ideal selection impossible of publication at present, except by piracy, even if such an anthology could be crowded into a single volume. However, this group of stories is thoroughly illustrative of the history, the structure, and the excellences of the short story; and in combination with the smallest public library, will supply the reading without which literary history is valueless.*

This book is intended also as a substitute for the author's *The Short Story,* published in 1902 as one of the *Yale Studies in English.* So much water has run under the bridges since then that it seemed better to write a new book, rather than to reissue a partial study.

NEW HAVEN, August 1, 1912.

* A comprehensive list of representative short narratives in the chief literatures may be found in Jessup and Canby's *The Book of the Short Story,* edition of 1912.

CONTENTS

ILLUSTRATIVE SHORT STORIES

THE SHORT STORY

I

WHAT IS A SHORT STORY?

WHEN a maker of fiction starts out to write or to tell a story, he must find a beginning, a middle, and an end for his narrative. It is a completed action that his audience asks for. The most typical instance of such a completed action is to be found in the life of a man, or a group of men, or the important details of that life; and it is of such a life-history that the modern novel professes to treat.

Yet within this unity of man's birth, achievement, and death are many lesser unities, none the less complete because they may be regarded as parts of a whole. The hopeless love which binds together a few episodes of some otherwise not extraordinary life into a significant story; the unexpected situation quickly developing, quickly passing away; these are strands which can be drawn from the web of possible experience. The term "short story," as it is used in current writing and speech, does not mean a story which merely *happens* to be short; it is applied to the narrative which covers such a lesser unity. A lesser unity, of the kind I have described, makes the *substance* of a short story; the *form* is what such a subject demands: a brief narrative, all of whose constituent parts unite to make a single impression upon the mind of the reader.

In the earlier periods of English literature the distinction between the short story and other forms of narrative is better marked in subject than in form; and it is often impossible to draw a dividing line between the short tale and the long. The saints' legends and the short romances, for instance; it is often impossible to classify them. But as narrative grows more and more sophisticated, the separation is ever clearer and clearer, until to-day not only the subject, but also the manner of telling, of the short story set it apart with sufficient, usually with remarkable, definiteness from other kinds of fiction.

However, the marking of boundaries need not be taken too seriously by the lover of the short story. That is a task for a rhetorician, and a patient one. It is enough for us to recognize that in all periods there have been stories told of life's lesser unities, and that, since literature became self-conscious, these narratives have been felt to constitute a class or department of their own. In their many varieties they have often been named by the ages or the races which enjoyed them, and it is the existence of such well remembered *genres* which makes the study of the short story something very different from an attempt to distinguish between short tales and long ones. Sometimes the name indicates a characteristic form and spirit, as in the Italian *novella,* sometimes a definite subject, purpose, and form, as in the fable, where a moral for man is drawn from a short story of beasts. Sometimes the name is of a transient kind, as with the *lai,* which was merely a Celtic fairy-tale given form in French verse. Again, there may be a distinctive variety with no really distinctive name, as in the case of our own short story, which differs in substance, and especially in form, from all earlier attempts to give a single impression of a lesser unity.

The history of the short story in English is a history of such of these varieties as have appeared from time to time in English and American literature. There has been no real evolution among them. They come from change and experiment. They represent, at most, a slow development, with some retrogressions and many fresh starts. New varieties have come in from abroad, or have been devised at home; have prospered according to their fitness for the needs of the age; have declined and given place to others. Five times at least the wave of a foreign culture or a foreign civilization has brought a new short story with it into England, and twice in England and once in America a new form has been developed by native writers. These varieties are not all equally important as literature, however they may rank in the historical development of a type. There can be no adequate understanding of the short story in English without a survey of the successive experiments, successful and unsuccessful, which have followed one another throughout so many centuries. But it is from the early nineteenth century onward that the short story becomes most significant in English literature, most important and most interesting for us; and it is with this period that the following pages will more especially deal.

II

THE MEDIEVAL SHORT STORY

THREE famous collections of stories, the *Gesta Romanorum* (? 14th century), originally in Latin, and of unknown authorship, Gower's *Confessio Amantis* (14th century), and Chaucer's *Canterbury Tales* (14th century), fairly sum up and fairly represent the medieval English short story. The first two contain all of its most notable varieties in very typical forms; the third registers the high-water mark of artistic perfection. The *Gesta Romanorum* and the *Confessio Amantis* represent that European literature of the short story of which England had its part; *The Canterbury Tales* contain the fruits of an individual English genius freely at work upon this literature. Let us outline the varieties of the medieval short story with these three great type-collections, and the examples they contain, as goal.

Earliest in point of time, most characteristically medieval in spirit and in substance, are the *contes dévots*. These little pious narratives seem to have originated with the Greeks of the early Christian centuries, who made short-story plots from the miraculous happenings of Christian mythology. From Greek they passed into Latin. Then the most gifted of medieval races, the French, took these miraculous anecdotes, for they were little more, and from them made exquisite verse-stories, in which the imagination of the French poet worked freely upon his old plot. The process was not different from that by which the Greeks and Romans wrought their myths into artistic forms.

To the old stories the French writers added many new ones, the greater number inspired by the growing cult of the Virgin Mary. These stories spread to England, both in great cycles of *Miracles of Our Lady,* and in *contes dévots* of other saints, or, again, as separate tales of a miracle which had happened to a layman, a monk, a nun, or a priest. In England they permeated all the literature of the church. *The South English Legendary* has many, Robert of Brunne's quaint and instructive *Handlyng Synne* (1303) has many; but the most charming of the earlier specimens are to be found in the ruins of a great collection which was copied into the Vernon manuscript

(*E. E. T. S.* 98). One of its few surviving stories recounts how Our Lady "drew out" a new leg for her worshipper who had lost his by disease; another how she cured a quinsied monk by milk from her own breast; and a third is the dubiously moral tale of a monk who ran wanton in his wilde-hede, yet was saved from hell-fire because he said his Ave Maria each night before he started on his rakish way. But these naïve and simple tales are only preliminary to the supreme English composition in this mode, Chaucer's *Prioress's Tale,* of the little clergeoun whose throat was cut by the envious Jews, and who, thanks to Mary, was restored to sing Alma Redemptoris loud and clear. Simply told, earnestly told, not consciously fictitious, yet with a good plot, these stories are myths just passing into artistic form. And this, indeed, is the characteristic of the *conte dévot.* No remnant of our earlier literature is more charming, and more redolent of medievalism.

Scarcely less naïve than the *conte dévot,* quite as charming, but much rarer, was the *lai.* The *lai* was a Celtic fairy-story which had been given form and orderly development in French verse. It was born and named in the twelfth century, and to a mysterious Frenchwoman, Marie de France, probably of the English court of Henry II, we owe the best examples. But one, at least, was done in the English of the thirteenth century, the excellent *Orfeo and Heurodis,* a verse-story in which the old legend of Orpheus and Eurydice has been medievalized and transferred, with a Celtic glamour, to the faery world. More *lais* appear later, of which the finest is Chaucer's *Wife of Bath's Tale,* where the fairy-hag transforms herself into beautiful youth for the knight who gives her sovereignty over him. Gower tells the story in his *Florent,* more directly but with less charm.

Except in grace, melody, and wisdom, these later writers do not excel the simple tale of *Orfeo*.

Much closer to the heart of the Middle Ages is the *fabliau*, a story of humor and realism, which served the frolic or the satiric mood as the *conte dévot* served devotion, and was at the opposite pole from romance. The "good story," told from the earliest ages, was the root of the *fabliau;* its plot was often immeasurably old; but its verse form, its elaboration, its flavor of a specific age, came at the hands of French minstrels in the twelfth and the thirteenth centuries, and to such verse-stories alone is the name properly applied. In French many survive, in English, before Chaucer, but few, although there is every reason to suppose that once they were plentiful.[1]

But whatever may have existed of English *fabliau* before Chaucer sinks into insignificance beside his transformation of this variety of the short story. His masterpieces, *The Miller's Tale*, of a reeve duped by his wife, *The Reeve's Tale*, of a miller tricked by two Cambridge boys, and *The Merchant's Tale*, of old January and his frail but lovely May, offend against modern taste in their indecency, but this indecency belongs to the satiric, cynical, eminently realistic *fabliau*. Indeed, they are more indecent, as they are more vigorous, more true to character, more picturesque, and more witty than any other *fabliaux*, whether in French or in English. Furthermore, there is a consummate art in these stories which more than makes up for their grossness. Chaucer had trav-

[1] Of the early ones that remain only one is noteworthy: the quaint tale of *Dame Siriz* and how, by trickery, she overcame the chastity of a credulous wife. In a dialect so far from modern English that it can be read only by a student of the period, this story has nevertheless enough homely vigor of style, and flavor, to give it a humble place in English literature.

eled to Italy; had been touched by the spirit of the earliest Renaissance; had acquired that interest in individual human nature which the full Renaissance was to spread. In these *fabliaux* the human nature of the Middle Ages comes to life with all the trappings of individuality. The humorous reflection upon life which is at the root of this short-story form flowers forth in satiric comment upon character and upon life; the *fabliau,* in short, develops its full potentiality and becomes one of the most successful forms of the short story. Unfortunately, Chaucer, and only Chaucer, was able to do all this, and these Canterbury *fabliaux* have had few successors and no rivals.

But there is another kind of *fabliau* in *The Canterbury Tales,* the *Nun's Priest's Tale* of beauteous Pertelote, of Chauntecleer, and of the fox that beguiled him. This tale is descended from the famous beast-epic; no epic, indeed, but a vast collection of stories originating in France, in which the lion was king, the fox the villain, the wolf the dupe, and the donkey the victim.

In spirit and in form a *fabliau,* narrowing its range to a little world of animal actors, but closely and satirically reflecting the real world outside, the beast-*fabliau* was a thoroughly medieval invention. The unknown author of *The Vox and the Wolf* (13th century) has given us the earliest in English. His, at most, is an adaptation from the French. Chaucer's is infinitely more original, and for the reader not skilled in Middle English his story is by far the best example of the type. But, fortunately, in this case another man was born before the end of the Middle Ages, who had the power to repeat and vary Chaucer's achievement, and we must bring him in, even though we go beyond our three collections to do so. The so-called fables of the Scotchman, Henryson, who lived in the fifteenth century, when so much of medievalism was stale, are fables only in name or in origin. In spirit and in execution they belong to the undidactic beast-*fabliau,* told not to drive home a moral, but humorously to mirror life. The humor of the beast has never been better seen than by this Scotchman; only Chaucer excels him in quaint charm of phrase; the former's version of the tale of Chauntecleer and Pertolote has touches which even Chaucer does not equal. He must rank among the great humorists; unfortunately his dialect will forever exclude him from the popularity which he deserves.

Closely allied to the *fabliau,* differing often only in mood, are the many medieval short stories in which human nature, but human nature in its less amusing aspects, is the basis of the plot. Such stories in prose form are numerous in the *Gesta Romanorum,* and many a good tale, handed down as history, belongs to this class. The Middle Ages had no definite title for them: perhaps the term "novella," used later by the Italians and the Germans for like short narratives, will serve usefully as a name. Latin collections of exemplary stories, so common in this period, are full of brief, inartistic specimens; Gower has many, usually of a quasi-historical nature; but Chaucer's wonderful *Pardoner's Tale* is the supreme example of such a narrative, done in the full medieval spirit, yet artistic to the highest degree. This is the tale of the three who poisoned and murdered each other for gold, a concise and vivid narrative which, once read, is never forgotten. It is from human greed that the story springs; yet it is not so much the moral as the action which one remembers: the old man knocking for admission upon the earth, which is his mother's gate; the three roisterers setting out so defiantly to seek Death, who awaits them by the pile of gold. And this is characteristic of the *novella.* It was this kind of short story which, with like substance, but a somewhat different form, was to have so great a success in the Italian Renaissance.

These story varieties, so far considered, are all undidactic; but the Middle Ages loved the story with a moral. They practised abundantly the apologue, which is a short story based, as is the *fabliau* or the *novella,* upon human nature, but told for its moral, not for its plot; and the fable, which is a like story, with beasts instead of men for actors. It would be interesting to discuss the remarkable popularity of these narratives; especially of the fables, which, descending from the Orient and the classic civilizations, spread through all the medieval literatures. But fable and apologue alike were too closely bound to the service of a work-a-day didacticism to attain literary merit. The humor which illumined the fable-like beast-*fabliau,* and the imagination which sometimes filled that other didactic type of the Middle Ages, the allegory, never transformed these humble stories into art.

Yet there was one mode—variety is scarcely the word—of the medieval short story whose didacticism had far-reaching effects. A practice of collecting short stories which could be used as illustrations in sermons was formally begun in the twelfth century. By the thirteenth and fourteenth centuries this had reached enormous proportions. Vast collections of so-called *exempla* were compiled in Latin and alphabetized for preachers' ready use. Handbooks of morality, like the *Handlyng Synne,* already mentioned, were compiled in the vernacular, consisting chiefly of *exempla,* each illustrating a point of morals or of doctrine. The *exemplum* spread through all ecclesiastical literature, and was imitated by secular writers. The *Gesta Romanorum* is nothing but a collection of *exempla* with a high percentage of the profane, and a low of the religious, in its narratives. The *Confessio Amantis* in its plan imitates a handbook of morality, with discourse of love in place of discourse of doctrine, and with much the same kind of stories, though better told. The Canterbury pilgrimage itself is full of evidences of this influence. *The Monk's Tale* is a collection of *exempla; The Pardoner's Tale* an *exemplum* which professes to illustrate the sermon which precedes it, although actually it was the story for which Chaucer cared. All varieties of short narratives except the most indecent and the most frivolous were swept into the *exemplum*-monger's net; so that, as *exempla,* you may expect to find every type of medieval short story. And these stories were rid of superfluities, pulled together, sharpened, as it were, so that the moral application, which had often to be forced upon them, should not lack its point. This, one sees, was a very training-school for the effective short story. And one observes, with a dawning realization of the literary importance of this practice, that the majority of medieval short narratives at one time or another were put into this strait-jacket, and that the short story continued to bear, in general, an exemplary character until the beginning of the nineteenth century.

With due recollection of the history of these several varieties of short story, thus briefly outlined in the preceding paragraphs, the reader who wishes an introduction to the medieval short story in English may best get it in the three works mentioned at the beginning of this chapter.

He should go first to the English translation of the *Gesta Romanorum,* for the homely but effective stories of this great collection represent the various medieval subtypes in unadorned, unliterary form. Here, nevertheless, he will find some of the best plots, and furthermore, he will see the stock in trade of the short-story teller before individual talent had begun its work.

The *Confessio Amantis* will give him again stories which are exemplary in form, but this time told more wisely, as befitted the scholar who was their author, and more elaborately, and more beautifully, for Gower was a man of letters, too. Furthermore, art and individuality begin to work upon the stories in this collection, though neither to an overwhelming degree. Yet Gower, though a tiresome disputant, is a pleasing story-teller. The plan of his work excludes the lighter narratives, the *fabliau* and the fable, but, except for their absence, there is no better book in which to gain a comprehensive view of the wide field of the medieval short story. That the narrative in the *Confessio Amantis* is untouched by genius makes it all the more typical of its age.

It is to Chaucer most of all, however, that the student should turn for an acquaintance with the medieval varieties. In *The Canterbury Tales* he will find the best of the short-story kinds of the Middle Ages, with all that their centuries had given them, plus the additions of a great genius. Neither the French, who, in the twelfth and thirteenth centuries, crystallized these sub-types, nor the Italian Boccaccio of Chaucer's own century, can bear comparison with him in sheer story-telling. The feeling for individuality, the sense of reality, the instinct for the essential word or action which drives home the plot, these attributes of the great story-teller of any age, Chaucer possessed, and employed them not in new fields, but in the familiar story fashions of his own period. It is true that he was inspired by a breath of the earliest Renaissance, that he was smitten with the passion for man, which was also Shakespeare's. But although this and his own genius set him apart from his predecessors, yes, and from his contemporary, Gower, yet he worked with their tools, and kept himself to the provinces which they had conquered for the short story. Better than any other writer, he can bring a modern into sympathy with the narrative of the Middle Ages.

After Chaucer came a century of decline, with only one vigorous contributor to the literature of the short story, and no new varieties.[2] The unliterary *exempla,* to be sure, flourished more abundantly than before, and, indeed, it is in this fifteenth century that the *Gesta Romanorum* was first Englished. *Fabliaux, lais,* apologues, *contes dévots* were perpetuated by minstrels and ecclesiastics in debased versions, which have little worth except as evidence of earlier and better progenitors. The writers who carried on the literary tradition of the English short story were Lydgate and Occleve, but no narrative of theirs has more than historical value. In Scotland, story-telling retained some of its vigor, and the so-called fables of Henryson, already mentioned, have virility and high artistic excellence. Of him one can scarcely speak too highly. But this is the end of the medieval short story. After Henryson, and his compatriot, Dunbar, there is no more short narrative of distinction until the sixteenth century and the Renaissance.[3]

[2] The medieval period saw the entrance into written form of one kind of narrative, the ballad, which was destined for high appreciation—after many centuries. But the ballad is essentially lyric in its inspiration; only in its more debased forms does it become primarily narrative. Therefore it is better left out of this accounting.

[3] In this brief survey of the medieval short story I have omitted, as seems just, all reference to the stories of the borderland between long and short narrative: the short romances, for example, such as the French *Aucassin and Nicolette,* since they may be studied more satisfactorily in connection with the class to which

III

THE SHORT STORY OF THE RENAISSANCE

THE sixteenth century saw the end of the old order of fiction. In the latter half of that century this literature, which had received its form and its types from France, the intellectual leader of the Middle Ages, gave place to a new fiction, borrowed indirectly from Italy, the mother of the Renaissance. In this fiction the short story was paramount. It resembled the medieval short story in that its form and spirit came from abroad; it differed in that no master, like Chaucer, came to develop its full possibilities. Instead, as we shall see, it gave all its vigor to the drama and to other literary forms, passing away finally without achieving a masterpiece of the first order.

It was the so-called *novella* of the Italians which brought in this new fiction. The *novella,* in a typical form, is still familiar in *The Decameron* of Boccaccio. That work, though composed in 1353, before *The Canterbury Tales,* and long before the coming of the Renaissance to sixteenth-century England, is the prototype of the many collections which succeeded it, and which poured their wealth into England. The stories of *The Decameron* are in subject not all short stories. Many have the larger organism of what the French call the *nouvelle*—some, indeed, are condensed romances. This

in spirit and in substance they belong. Nor have I noted the continual cross-reference between the varieties of the true short story: the *conte dévot* which is half apologue; the *lai* which is half *fabliau;* this in the interest of greater simplicity. For a detailed discussion of the whole period, with full bibliographical details, see *The Short Story in English,* Chapters I-V.

was also true of the medieval collections. But all are written with brevity and point. They are, in truth, exemplary stories, but though not differing from the best of the medieval *exempla* in form, all are infused with a freedom of observation, a passion for life, and an interest in places and in character which denotes work of the Renaissance. The later *novelle* of Bandello, of Straparola, of Cinthio—names familiar to us because of their association with the plots of Shakespeare's plays—do not differ strongly from these narratives of Boccaccio, except that their stories retain less of the character of *exempla,* and draw more freely upon historical anecdote. Thus the Italian *novella* was a short prose story, in short-story form, though not always with a short-story subject. But, more important, it was a vehicle for the conveyance of all manner of fresh observation upon life and character. It was this which made it appeal to the English of the Renaissance.[4]

Professor Schelling has made clear in his recent book on Elizabethan literature that the Elizabethan age must be regarded as a period of translation as well as of creation. The proportion of this ardor for translation which was spent upon the *novella* can be judged from the angry scoldings of such moralists as Ascham, who thought that the new story was too warm for the youth of England. The monuments which remain, numerous as they are, represent but a part of the work. It is certain that from 1566, when Painter Englished his collection of French and English stories, until the end of the century, the *novella,* in translation, imitation, or adaptation, was the popular fiction of Englishmen.

William Painter's book, *The Palace of Pleasure*

[4] For a general discussion of the sources of the Renaissance short story, see *The Short Story in English,* Chapter VI.

(1566-67), will serve as an example of this *novella,* as it first appeared in English dress. *The Palace* is a voluminous collection adorned by selections from the chief *novella* writers of Italy, reinforced by narratives from the French, most of which had more remotely been Italian, and enriched by tales from Herodotus and other classic authors, which resembled in substance and in form the Italian stories. I give the quaint sub-title of one narrative whose plot was destined to greater fame than Painter, or his French and Italian predecessors in the telling, could give: "The goodly Hystory of the true, and constant Love between Rhomeo and Julietta, the one of whom died of Poyson, and the other of sorrow, and hevinesse: wherein be comprysed many adventures of Love, and other devises touching the same." After an introduction which says that at Verona scarcely "their blubbred eyes be yet dry, that saw and beheld that lamentable sight," the story begins: "When the Senior Escala was Lord of Verona, there were two families in the Citty, of farre greater fame than the rest, as well for riches as Nobility: the one called the Montesches, and the other the Capellets: but lyke as most commonly there is discorde amongs theym which be of semblable degree in honour, even so there hapned a certayne enmity betweene them: and for so mutch as the beginning thereof was unlawfull, and of ill foundation, so lykewyse in processe of time it kindled to sutch flame, as by divers and sundry devyses practised on both sides, many lost their lyves." A love intrigue supplies the plot of most of these stories. They are simply written, with few digressions, few flourishes, and little or no originality on the part of their translator. Personality finds little place in them, for it was the plot and not the characters which interested their writers, and yet they savor of real life, especially the tales from France and Italy, and are full of potentiality. In England, these foreign tales were the first successful short stories in prose; they were the first successful transcript into literature of the men and women of the new epoch.

Painter's stories had a great vogue. Many collections of the same kind followed, and some writers of the day, Gascoigne, for example, went so far as to put forth original narratives purporting to be, like Painter's, translated from the Italian. But, unfortunately for the short story, though fortunately for English literature, the men of original talent who now entered the Elizabethan field were dramatists, not story-tellers; or, if they were both, were usually more vigorous and more original in the drama than in fiction. They turned prose to poetry, and raised fiction to their stage. *Romeo and Juliet, The Merchant of Venice, Othello,* are edifices much more vast and infinitely more rich than the *novelle* from which they were derived. Thus almost from the moment of its introduction, the new short story began to be transformed into another type of literature in which the Time Spirit of the Age, so it proved, was to find itself more at home.

But the Elizabethan short stories were not without an excellence and a literary development of their own. Though far less successful than the best of the drama which was made from them, these narratives held many a cupful of pleasure for our ancestors, and may for us. In the beginning they were good stories well and simply told, with the ringing plot and the possible characters which give permanency of value. And when they had entered upon the strange development now to be recounted, they became, at the expense of an opportunity to become great fiction, almost the most Elizabethan of Elizabethan literature.

The important agents in the literary development of the Elizabethan short story were Painter, Fenton, Pettie, Lyly, and Greene. Painter's famous *Palace* was followed in 1567 by the *Tragical Discourses* of the ambitious young courtier, Geoffrey Fenton. These histories, ten in number, had once been fairly compact *novelle,* of a semi-historical character, included in a collection of Lombard tales by Bandello, a fifteenth-century resident of Milan. Before they came to Fenton's eyes they had been worked over by Belleforest, a French scholar and humanist associated with the famous *Pleiad* who tried to make over French verse. A scholar and a rhetorician, Belleforest had applied to these simple Italian stories all the art, all the knowledge, and, one may add, all the pedantry, which humanists were lavishing upon the vulgar tongues in the attempt to raise them in dignity and in ornament to the level of classic Latin. Bandello's straightforward *novelle* emerged like a plain man in an academic gown and hood. They were double the length, stuck full of elegant similes, choice allusions, and polite discourses on the subject nearest the heart of the Renaissance, the proper conduct of life. Now it was ten of these inflated stories that Fenton took over into English. The rhetorical he made more rhetorical; to the discourses he added discourses of his own in a style whose pompous sonority showed his ambition to make these narratives literature; and, so doing, he seems to have pointed the way for Elizabethan fiction. *The Countess of Celant* was probably his masterpiece. It is a horrible story of love and crime, upon which is raised a framework of letters, orations, and moral comment, the whole finished off with classical allusion, intricate simile, and every device which the rhetorician could command. Tiresome, yes, but interesting, too, for it was the beginning of one of the most curious diseases with which a literature was ever afflicted.

The next important step is to be found in a highly curious book written by George Pettie, and called *The Petite Pallace of Pettie His Pleasure* (1576), now very rare. But it is more than a literary curiosity, for it shows what was to be English originality in this form of fiction. *The Petite Pallace* is another story collection. Pettie took his plots at random, with a preference for classic stories, but, as was the custom in Italy, worked them out with every emphasis upon intrigues in love. His chief interest, however, was in ideas, and in every kind of argument for which his story could give an excuse. He takes the old tale of Admetus and Alcest, retelling it with a maze of love-letters in which the plot is lost. He takes the favorite medieval legend of Alexius, and makes it a vehicle for a discussion as to which is better, study and meditation, or a wife. He writes of Germanicus and Agrippina as an excuse for urging virginity. Furthermore, all this is in a highflown style, employing every rhetorical device that prose allows, and some, such as rhyme and regular rhythm, which even Elizabethan prose did not permit. Pettie was, indeed, Euphuistic; and his more popular and more famous successor, John Lyly, was but little more so in the book which gave our language the word.

It was in Lyly's *Euphues* (1579-1580) that this strange development reached its culmination. *Euphues* consists of two parts, through which float innumerable letters, arguments, similes, and allusions upon a scarcely moving stream of narrative. Subtract the plot, and there would still be a great mass of material, such as we might put into conversational essays like those which Lamb liked to write. But the comparison is misleading, for no age since the Elizabethan could have conceived such rhetorical elaboration of every topic popular in the Renaissance as makes up Lyly's book. I give an example, chosen from what Lyly seems to have meant to be concise and rapid dialogue. The lover speaks: "Lady, to make a long preamble to a short sute, wold seeme superfluous, and to beginne abruptly in a matter of so great waight, might be thought absurde: so as I am brought into a doubt whether I should offend you with too many wordes, or hinder my selfe with too fewe. She not staying for a longer treatise brake me offe thus roundly. Gentle-man a short sute is soone made, but great matters not easily graunted, if your request be reasonable a word wil serve, if not, a thousand will not suffice. Therefore if ther be any thing that I may do you pleasure in, see it be honest, and use not tedious discourses or colours of Rhethoricke, which though they be thought courtly, yet are they not esteemed necessary: for the purest Emerauld shineth brightest when it hath no oyle, and trueth delighteth best, when it is apparayled worst." Alas, "discourses" and "colours of Rhethoricke" are the rule, not the exception, in this remarkable volume!

Clearly the story element is on the way to extinction in *Euphues;* and, indeed, with Lyly, and his chief follower, Robert Greene, the Elizabethan imitation of the Italian *novella* came to an end. The plots, overweighted with all the learning, the curiosity, and the gossip of the Renaissance, gave way, and this dropsical short story was succeeded by essays, by collections of letters, and by those studies of typical "characters" which made Overbury and Earle famous. Nor is it possible to assign the origin of these popular forms of seventeenth century literature without considering that to some extent they crystallized out of the over-saturated *novella;* that they were a successful attempt to do with a free hand what the Euphuists were always trying at pauses in their stories.

Thus, to resume, the promising *novella,* having yielded up its plots to the dramatists, was delivered into the hands of the rhetoricians, who were writers for a society just coming to consciousness. Packed with the spoils of Renaissance learning, elaborated into preciosity, made to serve for everything but the telling of a story, it reached a limit of expansion, and then broke down, like an over-complex molecule, into constituent elements which formed new and more stable products. Its greatest achievement was *Euphues;* a book full of wit and sound sense which have to be sought for through the most artificial style ever invented, and a story almost utterly devoid of narrative interest.

In fiction, the romance, as we know it in Lodge's *Rosalind,* succeeded the short story. The real world of Italy or of England, which had grown dim in *Euphues,* gave place to an imagined scene in the Orient, the Antarctic, or the coast of Bohemia; and, in freeing themselves from the comparative reality of the Italian *novella,* the writers also freed themselves from the short story. In the stories of Robert Greene one can watch the transformation from compact Italian *novella* to loosely plotted Elizabethan romance.

THE SEVENTEENTH CENTURY

The Euphuized *novella* went out of fashion at about the end of the sixteenth century, in those years when Shakespeare was satirizing Euphuism in *Henry IV, Part I.* The short romance of Ford, Breton, Greene, and Lodge, which, in a sense, sprang from it, lasted much longer, was popular, indeed, well on towards the end of the seventeenth century. The so-called "character-books" reached their highest development in the early years of this century. But the "character," though short, is not a short story. Important as were their influence upon the work of the eighteenth-century essayists, and, indirectly, upon the eighteenth-century novelists, these carefully studied analyses by Overbury and Earle of flatterers, pedants, hypocrites, "roaring boys," or "a meere fellow of an house," had no plot, no progression, were, in truth, expositions, not stories at all. Yet they are indicative of the change which in the next creative age of fiction was to come over short and long stories alike.

But before we enter upon that eighteenth century, when creativeness began again to have full play, we must not omit to note one strange and interesting manifestation of the vitality of the Renaissance short story. In the years between the death of Charles I and the Restoration of 1660, the vast heroic romances of the French writers of fiction began to be popular in England. With them, as another sign of the substitution of French influence for Italian and Spanish, came also a shorter story, more probable than the extravagant romances, much more unified. "Novels" these stories seem most frequently to have been called. After 1660, translations of them became abundant; imitations followed; and, finally, in Aphra Behn's *Oroonoko* (1688), a truly original and really excellent example came from an English pen. These novels averaged, perhaps, a hundred pages in length, and in these pages the story got itself finished, an achievement the heroic romance could hardly boast of. The ruffled gallants who exchange compliments with their ladies and sword thrusts with their rivals, the tolerant morality, the elegance, the affectation, the decadent chivalry, are all of the age to which this literature belongs.

But in form these stories seem to have been a true development of the Italian *novella.* They preserve its unified plot—sometimes specific plots; its use of historic background; and its assertion of reality. They are more elaborate in incident; indeed, they are no more short stories in any strict interpretation of the term. *Oroonoko,* for example, is neither a novel in its scope, nor a short story in its subject. It is such a tale as Bandello or Boccaccio would have told with the brevity and compression of the short story, such a tale as the French, perhaps, would call a *nouvelle.*

The history of this "novel" of the seventeenth century; the part played by it in conveying French ideals of gallantry to England; its approach to a masterpiece in Mrs. Behn's story of a negro prince enslaved in the new world of South America; its unworthy career in the hands of profligate women in early eighteenth-century England, who wrote with the indecency, but without the wit, of the contemporary drama; most of all its gift to the true novel of Richardson and Fielding of the idea of a unified plot: all this deserves more space than can here be given. For our purpose, it is sufficient to note that with the passing in the mid-eighteenth century of this fashion of writing came the end of the Renaissance short story.

IV

THE SHORT STORY OF THE EIGHTEENTH CENTURY

Long before the brief "novel" of intrigue had ceased to be popular, a new kind of short narrative had sprung up in England, and this new variety was a true short story. In its fundamental characteristic it was not new; it was but a reappearance of the *exemplum,* and usually of the apologue appearing as an *exemplum.* But in art, and in its plot and characters, it differed from all English story types before or since.

The contributing elements which made possible this new experiment in fiction were all present by 1700. It was in the decades before the turn of the century that a critical spirit began to show itself in English literature. Writers such as Dryden, Congreve, Swift, Pope, are the products of a peaceful, settled, quite civilized society. In its essence their literary work, which was largely satirical, may be considered as a survey of English civilization to determine who is fit to live in such society, who is not. This critical attitude towards life brought with it an increased interest in the manners of the town, where civilization was more and more centering, and opened wide the gates for a study of morals in fiction. Next came a greater realism in narrative art, most strikingly manifested in the work of a journalist like Defoe,[5] but, after all, only the reflex of a strong reaction against religious and romantic enthusiasms. Last, but this came later, and began not much before 1700, was a revolt against the rakishness which had been so fashionable in Restoration society, and the unregulated habits which accompanied it, a revolt which was not so much against immorality as against bad taste in the conduct of life.

These three influences are all to be noted in what were perhaps the most notable literary productions of the eighteenth century, and in the new short story which they contained. In *The Tatler* (1709-11), and in *The Spectator* (1711-14), where the periodical essay took shape, the short story is often only imperfectly distin-

[5] For a discussion of Defoe as writer of realistic short narrative, see *The Short Story in English,* pp. 184-188.

guished from the graceful discussions of the quirks and quibbles of life which count for so much in these charming papers. Even so, it is clearly something new in narrative. A pendant to the essay, oftentimes no more than an anecdote telling how Flavia and her mother, Honoria, compete in the game of love (*Spectator* 91), it preserves in one crystal drop an essence of Queen Anne manners in a solution of human nature. It is studied from life, yet told for the lesson it carries. The famous De Coverley papers are not the best examples. They are too rich in imagination, too little shaped to the purposes of didacticism, to be typical of this periodical short story. The novel with its wealth of characters, and broad field unrestricted by the need of driving home a moral reflection, was the goal towards which they tended. But there are hundreds of little narratives in these two famous periodicals, and in the many succeeding imitations, which are so well directed towards a chastening of the follies of the day, that, although stories in miniature, and rich neither in characters nor in plot, their brevity in no sense brings triviality with it.

Addison's are the ripest and most graceful of these. And when he borrowed the Oriental apologue from the wealth of Oriental literature then rolling into England, or imitated it, as in *The Vision of Mirza* (*Spectator* 159), he was at his best in narrative. Yet the Eastern tales of *The Spectator* are necessarily deprived of the close application to contemporary England which was so characteristic elsewhere of this short story.[6]

[6] In all the short narrative of the period the Oriental apologue, borrowed or invented, is to be found beside the English tales. It differs from the other periodical narratives only in this: that while the English stories attempt to mirror English life, the Oriental deal with universal human nature under

But it was Dr. Johnson who crystallized this apologue of the periodicals. His stories in *The Rambler* (1750) are the finest example of this minor art. In the *Lingering Expectation of an Heir* (*Rambler* 73), or the bitter tale of *Misella* (*Rambler* 170-171), the narrative and the moral exactly balance, each lending point to the other; and one reads with pleasure and profit a well-balanced story which would never have been written save for the essay—often a dull one—which accompanies it. The art was minor, and yet, in its lesser way, it was admirable. Nowhere has reflection upon human nature been more perfectly and more unpretentiously embodied in narrative form. The best of modern short stories, with all their advantages of vividness, study of personality, and novelty of plot, may envy the measured adaptation of means to end, and the clear and simple development of these eighteenth-century apologues.

The successors of Dr. Johnson in this art of the didactic short story were such men as Hawkesworth in *The Adventurer*, Goldsmith in his *Citizen of the World*, and many of lesser fame and lesser excellence. In general, it was in close connection with the periodical essay that the most perfect work was accomplished. There are, it is true, many stories of independent composition, but either, like *Rasselas* and *Vathek*, they are scarcely short stories, or they are of inferior artistic merit. Naturally, then, the history of this short story continues as long as the periodical essay lasted, which was until the first years of the nineteenth century, and ends when the romantic revolt against the eighteenth-century attitude

a thin disguise of Eastern names, customs, and setting. Together, as they appear in the work of the periodical essayists, they make up what may be called the eighteenth-century type of the short story. See *The Short Story in English*, pp. 196-202.

towards life had conquered literature. The custom of didacticism is reflected strongly in the highly moral tales which were a part of Hannah More's *Cheap Repository Tracts* (1795-98), and less obviously in the very different kind of moral story which Miss Edgeworth wrote in the first decades of the next century. But, on the whole, the type, as established by Addison and Steele, and perfected by Dr. Johnson, continues with very little change until its extinction, and is not successfully imitated, or in its own field rivaled, by the moral stories which succeeded it. The reason for its relative excellence is the reason, also, for the narrowness of its development. In this century the true English novel had started upon its glorious career. To this novel the narratives of the periodicals had lent a study of manners, as the old *novella* had contributed the idea of a unified plot. The novel developed freely. But the short story, by custom, remained a pendant to the essay; was restricted to the purposes of illustration. In this age, as never before or since, it was bound up to the service of didacticism. Its range was small. Its success was remarkable.

V

THE SHORT STORY AND THE ROMANTIC MOVEMENT

THE short story of the nineteenth century, most distinctive and most fertile of all short-story varieties, was a very direct result of the so-called romantic movement in English temperament and English literature, a movement which, gathering headway all through the eighteenth century, reached its height in the days of Scott, Byron, and Keats. It was in pursuit of romanticism in the short story that America first produced fiction of excellent merit. It was in the romantic short story, which Americans were instrumental in perfecting, that the most interesting technical victories of nineteenth-century fiction were won.

The shaping influences were, if one treats the subject broadly, three in number. First, and by far the most important—indeed, a true creative force—the aforesaid romantic movement, generated in England, reinforced from Germany, and triumphing in the English poetry of the first decades of the century. It was the pressure of this romantic emotionalism, this new feeling towards life, upon all forms of activity, but most of all upon literature, which caused the new short story. Next in importance was a circumstance which strangely illustrated the energy with which this romanticism sought an outlet in fiction. In poetry, both lyrical and narrative, romanticism was eminently successful, and gave to English literature such masterpieces as the passionate odes and narratives of Keats, the weird tales of Coleridge, and the adventurous stories of Byron. In the novel it was no less successful, with the Waverley series as a supreme achievement. But the romantic short story in prose, except for the stately tales of Irving, which were modeled upon forms of an earlier epoch, failed, and, in general, failed dismally, because it lacked art. And it was, in a sense, this failure which made way for the commanding genius of Edgar Allan Poe. Finally, and this is a minor, but a very practical consideration, the vogue of periodical literature increased with every decade of the new century. The periodical essay, with its included short story, had passed, but the magazine, which likewise had its birth in the eighteenth century, was more elastic, and grew. It increased enormously in scope and influence in the early years of the century, and to it was added about 1825 a new (and a bad) periodical fashion, that of the annual, a Christmas giftbook made up of expensive engravings, sentimental poems, short familiar essays, usually trivial, and, most of all, short stories. That the vogue of the short story was a provocative of magazine and annual, is probable; that the existence of magazine and annual was a stimulus to short-story production, no reader who seeks the place of first publication of the famous tales of the nineteenth century can doubt.

The romantic movement gave a fillip to fiction, and especially to fiction which dealt with love, adventure, horror, pathos—all the typically romantic themes. The first results for the short story were, to put it mildly, unfortunate. They are to be found in the magazines of the Twenties and a little earlier, where an increasing number of short tales of strained love, of mawkish grief, of wild adventure, and especially of morbid or exaggerated horror begin to usurp the pages given over to narrative. When the fashionable and expensive annuals, *The Amaranth, The Keepsake, The Forget-me-not,* come into being, the abundance of these bad romantic stories is positively alarming. They seem to be experimental in nature; experiments in the attempt to make the short story carry the romantic spirit, and not very successful experiments, even the best of them.[7] They lack body, and they lack art. There were other experimental stories also: the combination of reflective essay and gentle narrative upon which Lamb was trying his delicate hand; De Quincey's more sonorous attempts in meditative romance; the wise Miss Mitford's slight but charming studies in village life. All of these experimenters revealed the new spirit of romanticism in some form, but,

[7] See *The Short Story in English,* pp. 212-216.

whatever else they may have accomplished, none of them can be said to have established a fertile type of short story.

Indeed, in the years between the beginning of this movement and Poe's first tale in 1833, only two writers really succeeded with the unadulterated short story. One of these was Scott, and though his *Wandering Willie's Tale* (1824) is a masterpiece of its kind, it is his only notable contribution. His unities were larger. But the other, Washington Irving, is first of all a writer of short stories. In the decade between 1820 and 1830, he accomplished what his many contemporaries of the magazines failed in; he took the romantic material of which his generation was so fond: the spooks, the marvelous happenings, hopeless love, "temperament," "atmosphere" generally—and made it into admirable short stories. He succeeded where so many of his fellow workers failed, because he had four qualities, in one or more of which most of his rivals seemed to be lacking: he knew a good short-story plot when he saw one; he knew how to develop it so as to preserve a perfect proportion of parts to the whole; he could grasp character; and he had a sense of humor. The humorous, reflective writers, Lamb and Mitford, had possessed little sense of plot; the romantic writers had been endowed with nothing but romance.

It is the admirable blend of humor and romance which keeps *Rip Van Winkle* and *The Legend of Sleepy Hollow* eternally fresh and eternally popular, while the lurid tales of mysterious horror which accompanied them rest undisturbed in the annuals and magazines. If you doubt the importance of humor, read some of Irving's unhumorous, over-romantic stories, such as *The Young Italian*. But form also played its part, form which was just what the short story of this period almost universally lacked. Form in the short story is not easily made manifest, and as we must take it up at some length when we come to Poe, we pass lightly here. Yet all readers recognize grace in telling a tale, and can see the careful proportioning, due emphasis, and laudable restraint, of Irving's two famous stories. Indeed, that lovable writer was too good a student of the typical master of the century of restraint and proportion, Addison, to be led astray often by romanticism, as were so many others of his time. His task was easier than theirs, for he filled his romantic plots with the good stuff of humorous character observation, while they were striving merely to produce a romantic effect with their narrative, something difficult of accomplishment until Poe had shown the way. But the intrinsic difficulty of that task is measured by the few who, in his time, were able to give a romantic short story worth or weight. He told the classic American stories, and he has given us one of the few great characters in American fiction, but the lesson he learned from the eighteenth century he could not pass onward. He established no school of the short story, and bad romanticism in small packages continued to stuff the annuals and the magazines.

VI

POE, AND THE FURTHER DEVELOPMENT OF THE ROMANTIC SHORT STORY

IRVING, it would seem, was too classic, too reserved for a generation craving excitement in its fiction. To judge from the bulk of what was published, the age wanted something more purely romantic than *Rip* or *The Legend of Sleepy Hollow,* and this desire seemed to grow. As has been said above, the periodicals of the time are full of hideous attempts to thrill the very nerve of romance itself. Stories of awful death, of pathetic bereavement, of mysterious adventure, follow upon one another in mawkish or in lurid succession. And artistically they are all failures. They try to achieve in prose the sheer romance which Coleridge, Byron, Keats had grasped in verse—and fail so markedly that one wonders whether the slim young ladies who lean upon tombstones or simper over rose hedges in the steel engravings of the annuals, could have been more than mildly excited by such hysterical pages.

Romantic periods are very prone to lack a sense of humor. A sense of humor is notably lacking in these stories. This, however, is not a serious charge, for the purest romance is also deficient in this quality, does not need it, in fact. The trouble with the sensational stories of the Twenties and the Thirties was not that they were unhumorous, but that, being unhumorous, they were not sufficiently romantic to make up for the absence of the good material of human nature which Irving, Scott, or Lamb could supply. They depended entirely upon a romantic effect, and this effect—it seems to us—they did not attain.

The people wanted it; that is clear from the number of attempts. Furthermore, to judge from the strained pathos, the exaggerated mysticism, the forced horror of the product, they wanted it "good and strong." There are many signs of decadent taste in the romanticism of between, say, 1830 and 1840. There is a touch of it in the lusciousness of Tennyson's early poems; still more in the romantic novel; most of all, perhaps, in short narrative. New effects are sought out to thrill jaded nerves, and the short story which now appeared was successful because it gave the greatest of new effects, because it made a successful appeal to the taste of a decadent romanticism.

This new short story was practically an invention of Edgar Allan Poe. By this I do not mean that he created the modern short story out of nothing, and, as the shorter catechism has it, all very good. On the contrary, nearly all the materials, most of the subjects, all the interests, were there; but it was left to him to combine them, or, in other words, to devise a means of telling. His work in the short story, which began apparently about 1832, followed naturally from the response of his genius to the desire of a public which wished a stronger variety of romanticism. His success was the result of his knowledge that an impression made strongly upon the intellect of the reader was the best means of exciting romantic thrills; and of his discovery of the means for conveying this impression through a short story. The Germans of the Romantic School, especially Hoffmann and Tieck, had gone one step beyond the hair-raising but not soul-stirring stories of the English writers. They had put an idea into their narratives and given them worth and carrying power. But Poe went further. He drove home his idea with a new kind of story-telling, and so presented a romantic world asking for stronger stimulants with a completely new sensation.

There was every reason why he should wish to do this. His work, as I have tried to show, was a natural outcome of the romantic movement. And, as will later be evident, it was particularly natural in America. Some one would have done it later, though probably far less completely, if Poe had not. This remembered, the reader is less likely to be shocked when told that this much-heralded short story was not new in subject. Its materials were just the themes of decadent romanticism, and the by-products of transcendental philosophy which were familiar in less imaginative form to all readers of the English romantic poets and the German story-tellers. It was really new only in technique.

What was this much talked of technique of Poe? Just this: Poe carried to the *n*th power an old principle of narrative, namely, suspense. Feeling that the romantic short stories in prose of his day did not get results (so one guesses), he chose beforehand (this he says himself) a certain effect which he wished to make, and then held the reader in suspense until, at the end of his story, and with all the force of accumulated interest, the desired effect was produced. The means he used can easily be described, and were easily imitated, although never, perhaps, with a success like the master's. Briefly, they consisted of a double device. First the interest was shifted to the end of the story, which was accomplished by making each sentence from the first on point forwards, sometimes in word, sometimes by suggestion, to that climactic moment which was to be the sum of the story. "The thousand injuries of Fortunato I had borne as best I could," he begins in *The Cask of Amontillado,* and never for an instant suffers the reader's attention to waver from the approaching, unknown tragedy which he feels is to end the story.

Next—and it is here rather than in structure that Poe excels his myriad followers—there is manifest a care that all the attributes of the story, characters, setting, and most of all the style, should lend their suggestive powers to the desired effect. That sonorous style which Poe could practise when at his best, which in his solemn stories, where these technical refinements are most essential, was most free from the bad taste to which he was sometimes liable, was, perhaps, the great factor in this second means of heightening suspense. It is like the orchestral accompaniment without which the artificialities of the opera may sometimes appear forced and crude.

Poe's approach to this consummate art, or artifice, for it partakes of the nature of both, can still be followed, though one must guess at the earlier stages. He began, as I said, by wishing to accomplish in prose what others had accomplished in verse. This was the intense excitation of the emotions, such an excitation as follows upon the reading of the fine sensuous poetry of the romantic period, notably such verse as is to be found in *The Ancient Mariner* of Coleridge, the odes and the tales of Keats, and the lyrics of Poe himself. This poetry *did* what the novelists and the short-story writers of the Twenties and Thirties in England and America had been so often trying to do. It gave a new sensation. It struck in to the mind and the heart. Poe, to judge by results, wished to do as much with prose; or, rather, he wished to do more, for the greater freedom of prose narrative offered great possibilities to the man who could learn to control it. One sees what appears to be an experiment in his early story, *The MS. Found in a Bottle* (1833). This narrative is a descriptive sketch rather than a story. It recounts an adventure, and, as there is no real plot to be developed to a solution, the problem of structure is not entirely worked out. The subordination of incident to climax, which is so notable in the later stories, is not so apparent as the art of tone. Description, character, style, are all chosen to contribute to the final impression of horror, so that this narrative, and the later *Descent into the Maelström* (1841) which resembles it, but is better done, are like perfect, if somewhat dismal, harmonies of somber purples and browns.

The next step forward seems to have been taken in

Berenice (1835), a story which would be atrocious, or, what is worse, ridiculous, if it were not so admirably done. Here, also, the art of tone is perfectly manifested. Every detail of the story, not less than the style in which it is written, suggests the morbid melancholy of a diseased imagination. But the new art of structure is also manifest. The incidents of a plot in which the disgusting hero is obsessed by the beautiful teeth of his cousin, and ravishes them from her corpse in the grave, all point forward to the horrible conclusion, all hold the reader in an artfully contrived suspense. *Berenice* is an example of decadent romanticism. It can never be ranked as the highest art, but its author shows that he has solved the problem of making one vivid impression with the short story.

Berenice seems to mark Poe's mastery of his technique, but it is in later stories, and far better ones, such as *Ligeia* (1838), *The Fall of the House of Usher* (1839), or *The Cask of Amontillado* (1846), that it developed its full capability. Let me repeat that only the art of perfect tone, which had already been used in poetry, and the art of suspense, which had been long familiar in narrative, are employed in the technique of these remarkable stories. But Poe's adaptation and refinement of these arts for application in the short story are so skilful that the result marks an epoch for fiction generally. *The Fall of the House of Usher,* for example: how the gloomy mood of the traveler, the desolation of the House, the peculiar super-attentiveness of the brother, the morbid mysteriousness of the sister, the flavor of the old romance, all merge, all point to the catastrophe, are all explained, and justified in their effect when overstrained nerves and weakened masonry giving way together, the House cracks apart, and, in the dim light of the blood-red sun, slides into the gloomy tarn! Imagine this story told otherwise than by suspense, a perfect tone, and a complete concentration: for instance, as Irving (who thought like thoughts, though less morbid and furiously intense) would have told it; or dragged out by the Germans (who conceived such scenes and such mentalities) through an interminable plot to a slow conclusion. No, in prose at least, it was only as Poe wrote that the effect could have been won.

It would be interesting to discourse of Poe's characters, of how false they are to life, and how true to the ultra-romanticist's imagination of life. It would be interesting to write of Poe's scenes and plots; his thought, his knowledge, and all that goes to make up the substance of his short stories. However, modern criticism, in general, seems to be agreed that it is not the characters which are valuable in Poe's stories, except in so far as they reflect Poe's state of mind; or the scenes, except for their beauty; or the thought, except as it explains the stories; or the plot; but, rather, just the vivid emotional effects which these narratives make upon the least imaginative readers. In other words, their value is artistic in the most limited sense. But these effects were made possible by technique, and, therefore, in so limited a chapter, to technique we must confine ourselves. Thanks to it, Poe was able to control the products of his superheated imagination, reduce them to order, and make them comprehensible by less intense (and less morbid) imaginations. A nightmare fancy of the plague-spirit, incarnate and walking among men, when harnessed to his short story became the orderly and sufficiently awful *Masque of the Red Death.* Vague speculations on the power of the immortal will, when bound down to his story-form became effective in the solemn and impressive *Ligeia.* Grant the urge of decadent romanticism towards all that was supernormal and sensational; grant Poe's sense of the beautiful, and his tremendous, if morbid, imagination; grant the stimulus of German transcendental thought, which drove directly towards the romanticist's conception of the mind of man; and then give credit for the very great portion of his success still unaccounted for to his discovery of how to perfect narrative suspense.

The results of this discovery are not confined to the use which Poe made of it. They are to be found in the various services to which this new way of telling a short story was applied after Poe had perfected it, and these must be carefully differentiated from his own practice. Let us leave this development for discussion in later sections, and complete this brief survey by consideration of another kind of short story in which Poe's work again was revolutionary. *The Murders in the Rue Morgue* (1841), *The Gold-Bug* (1843), and *The Purloined Letter* (1845), belong to the so-called detective-story class, although a detective figures in only two of them. What really relates them is the chain of reasoning which binds together each story, which makes each plot. Given a scrap of parchment written upon in cipher, to prove that the cipher refers to buried treasure, and to find the treasure—that is *The Gold-Bug*. Given a murder mysteriously done, to find the murderer—that is *The Murders in the Rue Morgue.* No need to run through the narratives, or to recommend them. Fortunately the taste for detective stories is more persuasive than tobacco. We all know them, and have probably a dim impression that stories of this general nature had been done before. The impression is correct. Poe did not discover that a process of reasoning makes a good narrative. Others were ahead of him there. But he did learn how to perfect the story into which such a process can be made.

The principle he worked with was again suspense. Observe, for example, *The Gold-Bug*. There is first the mysterious insect, and then the mysterious actions of the finder, and then the mystery of the parchment, and so on, until the hero at last satisfies our curiosity and ends the story. This suspense, it is true, though it is like the suspense of the impressionistic stories, is not used for the same purpose. No vivid impression of an intense emotion is planned for in these detective tales; the author cares only to increase the reader's interest with each step of the plot. And although they have given rise to a numerous progeny, they have scarcely been so influential as the impressionistic short story, which brought eventually not one, but many provinces to fiction. However, it is an error to consider these two varieties of Poe stories separately. Both sprang from one imagination and one mind. The stories of ratiocination reveal the keen sense of cause and effect which alone could have made Poe able to devise the construction upon which *Usher* and *Eleanora* depend for their success.

Of Poe the man, Poe the stylist, and Poe the student of supernormal human nature there is, unfortunately, no room here to speak. Again, his lack of humor and his occasional bad taste, although they affect slightly, if at all, his masterpieces, are instances of characteristics personal to him, or belonging to his time, which should accompany a complete analysis of his work. But whatever may be the final opinion of the critics who now so clamorously disagree, one fact should be clear—that Poe's work is decadent, that its romanticism is exaggerated, sensational, strained, if not overstrained. And, furthermore, whatever else they may decide, it should be equally clear that his artistic powers, which were far saner than his imagination, transformed his decadent material into beauty, which is often impressive and sometimes perfect.

Thus, while it will never be possible to place him in the first rank of the literary hierarchy, they do not wisely who would thrust him out. They are not wise because, when all is said, his decadent imagination was controlled by a vigorous reason. His stories, although the substance is often questionable, arouse in high measure the legitimate emotions of horror, terror, and awe; and both America and Europe have gone to school to his art.

VII

NATHANIEL HAWTHORNE

THE short stories of Poe and of Hawthorne are almost exactly contemporary. Both men came to artistic maturity in fiction about 1835, the date of publication of *Berenice* and Hawthorne's *The Ambitious Guest,* and Hawthorne's contributions to the short story ended a few years after the death of Poe in 1849. Furthermore, both writers were children of the romantic movement. Here the resemblance ceases. A closer relationship had never begun, for nothing is more significant of the originality of the American short story than the absolute independence of these contemporary masters, one of the other. Poe cared chiefly for emotional effects, and made in *William Wilson* (1839) almost his only experiment in moral analysis. Hawthorne moved in a world of moral thought, colored, but not dominated, by emotion. Poe devised a perfect technique in order that he might hold his stories together. Hawthorne's tales were prevented from flying apart only by his constant grip upon the moral situation, which was the nucleus of his story. The first was an artist working with the materials of decadent romance: the second a preacher employing as best he could the methods of art.

Heredity has seldom been more interestingly manifested than in the mind of Hawthorne. The single-mindedness of his Puritan ancestors, their deep concern with problems of grace, salvation, and of conscience, descended to him in full force, but in interesting transformation. Sin in its relations to salvation, questions of dogma, and the possibility of God's grace, no longer stir this liberal-minded Unitarian; problems of character, ethics, and the nature of the soul, have taken their place; but the habit of mind, the conscious introspectiveness of the Puritan, remains and becomes the prime characteristic of Hawthorne the man, the thinker, and the creative artist. In *The Ambitious Guest* it is the effect and the futility of ambition which interests him; in *The Birthmark* (1843) the failure of the search for human perfection; in *The Great Stone Face* (1850) the ennobling power of loyalty to a high ideal; in *Rappaccini's Daughter* (1844) the result of a poisoning of the mind. Upon such themes he dwells with an almost unexampled intensity. The stories which embody them have a little of the conventional and the commonplace, but they assume not a little of that moral majesty which we associate with the great Puritan work of the seventeenth century.

If Hawthorne had lived in the seventeenth century he would probably have preached. The romantic movement made a story-teller of him. His note-books show that he was constantly trying to clothe his moral themes in the garments of possible experience; and these garments were nearly always those of romance. Aylmer, in *The Birthmark,* is a magician who has all but conquered the secrets of life; Ernest, in *The Great Stone Face,* lives among wild mountains beneath a great face on a crag; the ambitious guest is swallowed up in an avalanche; Rappaccini's daughter is a Paduan nourished upon the poison of mysterious flowers; and no scene in literature is more romantic than the last hour in the life of Ethan Brand. The weird, the majestic, the awful, and the horrible: these familiar moods of the romantic movement all appear in such stories; and are quite as evident in the historical narratives. In *The Gray Champion* (1835), where the spiritual grandeur of the old Puritan subdues the pride of a royal governor, or *Legends of the Province House* (1838), his subjects, like Scott's, come from romantic periods of history, and the setting is in complete accord with what we recognize as the machinery of romance. Speculation upon moral problems is necessarily abstract: romance which is, in its essence, sensuous, demands the concrete. Over the bridge of romantic narrative, Hawthorne's thoughts upon human nature passed to the fullest artistic expression of which he was capable.

The passage was difficult. Take *The Birthmark* for an example. The moral idea at the root of this story is, as has been said, the futility of the search for human perfection. It was first expressed by Hawthorne in the form of a situation, and is recorded in *The American Note-Books,* under date of 1840, as follows: "A person to be the death of his beloved in trying to raise her to more than mortal perfection; yet this should be a comfort to him for having aimed so highly and so holily." As it stands, this moral situation could be made into either an allegory or a story. Hawthorne's romantic mind chose the latter. He imagined the wonderful laboratory of Aylmer, hung with gorgeous curtains; he imagined the tiny birthmark on the cheek of Georgiana; the foul dwarf, Aminadab, to play the cynic's part in the experiment; and then began the story of the fatal hand. If he could have made it all story! But no, he started with an abstract speculation, and he will not or cannot drop it. He enlarges upon his moral; he varies it; and then, at the very climax, when Georgiana's birthmark fades away in death, and the artist's work is done, "a hoarse chuckling laugh was heard again! Thus ever does the gross fatality of earth exult in its invariable triumph over the immortal essence, which, in this sphere of half-development, demands the completeness of a higher state. Yet had Aylmer . . . ," and so on to the didactic conclusion. The moral intensity of the writer is too great for his art. In the language of rhetoric, his narrative contains too much exposition. In the language of esthetics, he errs in subordinating art to the drawing of a moral. Smug the Joiner's head *would* peep from beneath the lion mask, and Hawthorne the preacher will interrupt even at the moment when Hawthorne the story-teller and romanticist is just casting his powerful spells. And, in varying degrees, this same error is to be found throughout *The Twice-Told Tales, Mosses from an Old Manse,* and *The Snow Image and Other Tales,* the volumes which contain his short stories.

So much for detraction. Yet it cannot be denied, even by the most bigoted believer in art for art's sake, that these solemn tales of Hawthorne have tremendous force. Their moral intensity, even when uncontrolled, gives them a weight and a dignity scarcely equaled in the short story, and the measured elevation of their style lifts them far above the banal and the trite. Even without the rolling music of Hawthorne's powerful style, it is questionable whether they could be trite. Hawthorne felt these familiar themes too deeply to be anything but impressive in his delivery of them. There was nothing novel in his thinking: no new speculations upon human nature seem to have come to him who was always speculating upon it, no new fields of imagining, morbid or otherwise, were opened by his fertile brain; but, like his spiritual ancestors, the religious enthusiasts of the seventeenth century, he struck fire into old truths, and turned white-hot again a familiar metal. Indeed, these moral stories, where the line between preaching and narration is often so insufficiently drawn, are finer, and seem to be more durable, than the more impressionistic, less speculative stories. *Ethan Brand* (1851), whose firelit gloom and tragic heart of marble in the ashes of the kiln drive home a sermon on egotism, is infinitely greater, far better remembered than *The White Old Maid* or *The Hollow of Three Hills,* in which the narrative is more subservient to the true end of art. The moral stories are finer because they have more of the true Hawthornesque. They alone, because of their sanity, because of their true human nature, but, most of all, because of their intensity, can be ranked with the much more artistic tales of Poe.

It is in these moral tales also that Hawthorne's contribution to the technique of the short story may best be studied. He was the first short-story writer to build his narrative purposefully and skilfully upon a *situation.* A situation may be defined as any active relationship between character and circumstances. *The Birthmark* has already given us an example. The *Note-Books,* under date of 1837, contain one quite as interesting, and quite as susceptible of development: "A woman to sympathize with all emotions, but to have none of her own." These *Note-Books* include many more, some of which were afterwards made into stories, others left undeveloped. Indeed, a moment's consideration of any Twice-Told Tale will reveal such a situation as the foundation of the narrative. In fact, it is the central situation which holds together each of Hawthorne's best stories; without it there would not be enough technique to keep the tale from flying apart.

This method of telling a story is of more than passing interest. The majority of modern short stories which have any claims to worth are built upon situations, though not often upon moral ones. Indeed, a situation makes a particularly good subject for a short story, and the life of the nineteenth century and our own has seemed to lend itself particularly well to this kind of literary treatment. Though later writers do not, like Hawthorne, require the unifying agencies of a single situation to keep their short narratives in a short-story form, yet many and many a vision of life could scarcely have been embodied in narrative except for this fashion of viewing it. The nineteenth-century interest in psychological problems would have quickly brought the method of the situation into the short story, even if Hawthorne's obsession with moral problems had not driven him to it first. And it was not a conscious art, like Poe's, which he developed; rather it came from his Puritan's eye, ever seeking the effect of the world upon character or the soul. Less spiritual writers could not, and did not, imitate that. But, though the direct influence of his kind of writing is much more difficult to trace than Poe's, its effects must be reckoned with; and the results in his own stories were superb.

A deep, if not an original, student of the heart, a great romanticist—for he makes moral problems no less than colonial governors romantic, a painstaking artist who labored to realize his conception of life, and failed only when the importance of his moral made him blind to the needs of his story, Hawthorne is one of the few great figures in American literature, and one of the most interesting in all the course of the short story. It is easy to criticize his tales; it is very difficult to forget them.

VIII

ENGLAND IN THE MID-CENTURY

In the third, fourth, and fifth decades of the nineteenth century two literatures were trying to devise a form of short narrative by means of which a single impression, a single situation, or a highly unified plot could be made intelligible and effective. The American writers, who dealt chiefly with impressions and situations, we have just discussed. The work of their French contemporaries, especially Mérimée, Gautier, and Balzac, was more especially with plots, and represents a parallel, not a derivative movement. Indeed, Mérimée, in such a story as *Mateo Falcone* (1829), had illustrated the art of single effect in a short story before Poe's first tale was published. American influence upon French narrative began much later, with Baudelaire's translation of Poe's tales in 1852-1865. The French short story had no marked influence upon American fiction until the last third of the century.

While these notable movements in story-telling were going on in both America and France, and, indeed, for nearly thirty years after the death of Poe in 1849, England contributed nothing new to the technique of the short story. It would be wrong to say that there were no short narratives of importance in the British literature of that period. On the contrary, there were many, but only a few of them belong to what we in our time call the short story. They may be assigned to three very well defined classes. In the first place, there are the numerous tales of Dickens, Thackeray, Mrs. Gaskell, later of Meredith and Hardy, which are neither long stories nor short ones. Dickens's *Christmas Carol* (1843) and *The Cricket on the Hearth* (1845) are typical of the kind to which I refer, and with them might be placed Mrs. Gaskell's charming *Cousin Phillis* (1863-64), Eliot's *Scenes of Clerical Life* (1858), and Meredith's *Chloe* (1879). No history of fiction could afford to neglect such admirable tales, and yet they have little place in the development of the modern short story. They are to be grouped with what the French call the *nouvelle,* a story of linked episodes, a larger unity than our short story, and lacking its singleness of effect, though in no sense attempting the complexity, the many-plottedness of the novel. Tempting subjects for critical appreciation, they belong outside the necessarily strict limits of our field. Not so with another kind of short narrative, rarely produced, it is true, in this English period, but also rare in its nature. I mean those admirable short stories which contain no artificial technique, no subtle situations carefully grasped, but just an unforced representation of a simple incident which itself has the high unity required for short-story success. Dr. John Brown's *Rab and His Friends* (1858), where modern surgery makes a most effective entry into fiction, is an admirable example. The third variety of mid-century English short narrative was less excellent. Under pressure from the weird and the terrible, those popular themes of romanticism, some English writers developed the art of suspense and the single effect which Poe, at an earlier period, had stamped his own, and turned out stories which in form, if not in substance, resembled those of the American. If one remembers the close connection between an urgent romanticism and the impressionistic short story, this will seem most natural. The surprising thing is that it was done so seldom. Dickens hit it off once in *The Signal-Man* (*Mugby Junction,* 1866); did it well, but only once. Wilkie Collins's *A Terribly Strange Bed* (1856), and Bulwer-Lytton's *The House and the Brain* (1859) are other specimens. All three of these are stories of horror or mystery. Nowhere, before the Seventies, was this technique, so far as I am aware, used for other themes. Thus the English writers, being, as a historian of fiction would say, busied with the more important business of the novel, and, as a believer in the American short story might add, somewhat inapt in the refinements of short narrative, had little share in the art which gave us that short story which, for better or for worse, has been typical of the turn of the twentieth century.

IX

AMERICA IN THE MID-CENTURY. THE BROADENING OF THE FIELD OF THE SHORT STORY

In America it was different, and naturally so, for there was a stronger incentive to short-story writing. There was the tradition of Irving, Poe, and Hawthorne, great writers whose fame was largely built upon the short story. There was a further impulse derived from the competition of the English novel, which was not only better than the American novel, but cheaper, since the lack of proper copyright laws allowed it to be pirated. The circulation of these imported goods discouraged would-be novelists, encouraged the magazines whose field was less easily occupied by a foreign competitor, and thus encouraged the short story, whose place of publication was usually in a periodical. Lastly, there was a wealth of short-story subjects in the rapidly changing civilization of this country, and, what was even more important, a disposition to grasp them on the part of American writers of fiction.

At first, although the short-story output was large, larger than England's, the quality was not high. In the mass of magazine stories published in the decade just before and just after the Civil War, there were many short stories of moderate excellence. But they are all highly inferior to the *nouvelles* of Dickens and the other experiments in short narrative of the English writers, although their subjects may make them interesting to an American reader. This, however, does not fully apply to work of two American writers of this period which is not only good in itself, but which continues that line of development which leads up from Poe and Hawthorne to the kind of story-writing which triumphed in the last third of the century. One of these men drew his inspiration from Poe. The other succeeded Hawthorne in the study of the situation.

Fitz-James O'Brien, an Irishman, migrated to America about 1852, and became a free-lance in journalism, poetry, and magazine fiction. His vigorous imagination, slightly morbid, and not untouched with Celtic mysticism, made him an easy victim to the spell of Poe. *What Was It?*, a story of an invisible monster who embarrasses the occupants of a New York boarding-house, and *The Diamond Lens,* the tale of the love of a youth for a microscopic creature who wrings his heart by dying in her world of a water drop, are his two best known stories. The stamp of the latter end of the romantic movement is upon these plots; the mark of Poe is upon the actors: morbid, abnormal people, who meddle with opium, or dally with scientific mysticism. And it is Poe's fine art of construction which makes the stories effective. Though

O'Brien did not catch the solemn beauty of Poe's style, though he descended from *Usher's* and *Ligeia's* regions of Gothic romance to prosaic New York, he achieved, nevertheless, a strong emotional effect. He was too imitative to be great; but when he imitated Poe's short story his success was well deserved.

Edward Everett Hale carried on the American short story in a different fashion. Hale was a Unitarian minister of varied capabilities, who lived until 1909; a fact which shows how rapid has been the growth of our now superabundant short story. His one great narrative is *The Man Without a Country* (1863), a story in which a poignant situation unifies the whole. Thus, in technique, he was a successor of Hawthorne. But he was in no sense an imitator. *The Man Without a Country* develops the situation of an unhappy lieutenant of our army who, in a moment of temper, wished to throw off his allegiance, and in a manner no less terrible than pathetic was granted his wish. Here is no moral problem, no attempt to give flesh and blood to abstractions, nothing, in fact, that is Hawthornesque, except the choice of a situation for the unifying principle of the narrative. It is an intensely patriotic story, all afire with the agonized loyalty of the North of the Civil War. Perhaps it is because of the gripping power of the central situation, that this ill-ordered narrative gives over the writer's intense emotion even to the readers of this later generation.

But one must regretfully note, in addition, for this mid-century in America, that of all its fertile story-tellers, none but these two have been kept in remembrance, and of these two, O'Brien has sadly needed a revival. N. P. Willis, Bayard Taylor, A. F. Webster, and many others have gone to the bookcase on the third-floor back. They had talent, wit; Willis, perhaps, a touch of genius. But their materials were too slight, their art not sufficient. The fortunate chance which made O'Brien a link between Poe and the modern short story alone has saved him from the general decay of reputations once excellent, for he was little more than a clever journalist. And the intensity of Hale's one great story alone makes it worth noting that the method of the situation was carried on there and elsewhere by that writer. But the experiments of these authors were more significant than, at this point in the discussion, they may appear.

X

BRET HARTE

It is more than noteworthy, it is remarkable, that until some time after the Civil War no one seems to have recognized that the impressionistic short story was particularly fitted to express American subjects. Perhaps it was because this literary form had been so closely associated with the mystic and the terrible of ultra-romanticism. It was Bret Harte who first applied the technique of Poe to distinctively American life; or, if you prefer, it was Bret Harte who first interested himself in the impressionistic features of a life distinctively American, and tried to put them into short stories. Furthermore, he combined with the emotional effect which Poe had desired that a short story should seek, the outlining of a distinct situation, in Hawthorne's fashion, and so established what might be called the normal method for the later short story.

A gold-mine as rich as the placer-beds was opened for this young American when, in 1857, he entered literature by the backdoor of a California typesetting room, and began to write in a new world full of vivid contrasts and striking situations. Subjects for short stories must have flashed upon him by multitudes, as they flashed upon the writers of that far deeper tumult, the Renaissance. At first he could not use them. His earliest tales make little effect. California was in them, but they do not make you feel California. Then he began anew. Perhaps he had been reading Poe. Perhaps he was moved by the need of driving his keen impressions home to the reader. Probably both. At all events, he wrote stories which he called "sketches," and the first of these was the famous *Luck of Roaring Camp* (1868), which shocked, by its vividness, the lady proof-reader of the *Overland Monthly*—strange proof that pioneer California was turning *bourgeois* at the very moment that its picturesque barbarism was first being effectively recorded. *The Luck,* with *The Outcasts of Poker Flat* and *Tennessee's Partner,* which followed in 1869, make up the great trilogy of Harte's stories. If all the rest of his prose had been left unwritten, his reputation would still rest quite securely, and, in truth, not much altered, on these three.

As literature, Harte's best stories crystallize the life of the mining-camp, a life where law was still a matter of personal opinion, and human nature could be seen working in the open, free for a time from many restraints. It is true that the wise say that Harte's California never existed. Naturally. He was a romancer, and, perhaps, a sentimentalist. He did not photograph, but paint. Certainly his version of this new world was sufficiently true to command applause, and more than sufficiently interesting. Few scenes in modern narrative are more convincing than the march of the exiles from Poker Flat, Tennessee's plea for his partner, or Roaring Camp's housewarming for its first baby. These glimpses of old human nature, revealing itself strangely in the midst of barbarism, lawlessness, license, and the Sierras, have a value which not even absolute untruthfulness to local conditions could utterly destroy. But, as H. C. Merwin, Harte's biographer, has recently proved, they are not untruthful; they are romantically true.

Again, there are the very memorable characters which Harte gave to fiction. There is the red-shirt miner with bad language, worse morals, and a big heart; the sweet-souled school-marm who serves as foil; and the generous gambler with steel-like nerve. These are not so American as the scenes and the life in which they move. Indeed, they belong to that world-wide family of sentimental characters in which the black and white of sin and virtue are mixed without being mingled. Dickens, Harte's chief literary master, was the adept among contemporaries in this art, and from Dickens, Harte learned much. Nevertheless, however sentimentalized, Kentuck, Oakhurst, Yuba Bill, were studied in California, and their reality is convincing. If the Forty-niners were to be presented typically, this method was, perhaps, most likely to catch the essential qualities of a society where the absence of conventions left human nature free.

Lastly, this interesting life, these picturesque characters and vivid situations, were embodied not in rambling tales from which half their flavor would have evaporated, but in well-ordered stories where incident led to incident, and the whole to a climax. Kentuck dead, with the baby's grasp still upon his great fingers; Tennessee pleading tearfully over the corpse of his villainous friend; Piney and the Duchess wrapped in each other's arms between the walls of Sierra snow, irresistibly make the desired emotional effect. Perhaps this is what Harte meant when he called these stories sketches. He knew that his purpose

prising situations: the story with a twist at the end. This story was a true product of the characteristic American humor which loves a sudden revelation of incongruity, especially if it be absurd incongruity. Mark Twain and his work sums up and represents this variety of humor so well that his name nearly defines it. His famous tale, *The Jumping Frog of Calaveras County* (1867), of the frog who couldn't jump because of the shot in his belly, is an early instance where the kind of tale I mean found its way into literature. But Mark Twain seldom troubled himself to turn his jokes into short stories. This enormously popular variety of fiction owes more to Thomas Bailey Aldrich, a charming artist, if not a great genius, who knew how to give the American anecdote sufficient body, and, what is more important, enough form, to raise its light fabric to the dignity of literature. His *Marjorie Daw* (1873), that tale of a fictitious sweetheart with its dramatic reversal at the very end, is not likely to be forgotten, and *Mademoiselle Olympe Zabriskie* (1873), of the acrobatic lady who ensnared an amorous aristocrat, and then proved to be a boy, is only less excellent. These stories, and the thousands that have followed them down to O. Henry and the generation of the ten- and fifteen-cent magazines, are really significant in American literature, for they inclose far better than the contemporary novel a characteristic, if not a vital, element of the American spirit. They embody the American's keen pleasure in the inconsequential and the ridiculous; in all that reveals man as mere man. It is the humor of a democracy. Perhaps the stories cited are too light to bear so heavy a text. But there have been thousands more. Frank Stockton was a jester of this vintage. His *The Lady or the Tiger?* (1882), which ends in a puzzle over which readers always disagree, made

comedy from a tragic situation. H. C. Bunner, with his frivolous but beautifully constructed *Short Sixes* (1891), followed—and then the names become legion. None, however, have equaled in style and in finish the work of Aldrich, although the spirit of fun has been carried much further afield than these earlier contributors to the American comedy endeavored to take it. Indeed, to a lack in finish is due the failure of the humorous short story in America to equal in its general development the literary merits of the parallel French school of Daudet and his followers, to whose methods, it may be said in passing, Bunner and Aldrich owed much. More of this when we reach our own time, into which a further discussion would lead us, for since the Civil War the field of American literature has been continuously cultivated for this variety of the short story.[8]

XII

THE LOCAL COLORISTS

THE use of local color is a logical result, on the one hand, of a growing scientific interest in the facts about our civilization, on the other, of the romanticist's interest

[8] There should be noted, under the further broadening of the short story, the remarkable work of a Californian, Ambrose Bierce, who is still writing. His *In the Midst of Life: Tales of Soldiers and Civilians* (1892) contains stories which combine Bret Harte's feeling for localities, with a Poe-like intensity of technique. His *Can Such Things Be?* (1893) is a collection of studies in mystical horror which are like the work of a more scientific, less artistic Poe. It is in the stories of the first group, however, notably in *An Occurrence at Owl Creek Bridge,* and *A Horseman in the Sky,* that the remarkable technical power of this author, and his grasp of psychological experience are best exhibited.

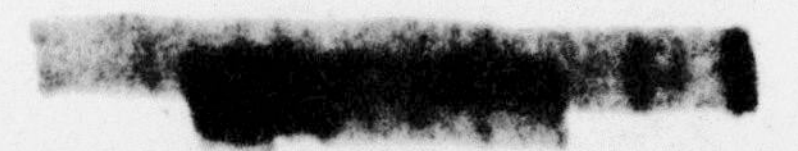

in the individual and his peculiarities. Local impression, its other name, indicates, what is very true, that in art it is very likely to be expressed by impressionism. Since it sprang, then, from currents running internationally throughout the nineteenth century, there is nothing local to America in the use of local color. But it was here that the workers in this field made use more especially of the short story, finding in it an instrument peculiarly adaptable to their desires. Harte was their forerunner. I say forerunner, because with him local color was a means rather than an end. In later decades the best workers went far beyond him in the depth and truth of their depiction, though falling short in narrative skill, and often in art.

The local colorists can be classified, like wheat or apples, by their districts. The first notable success after Harte was won in Louisiana by G. W. Cable, whose *Old Creole Days* (1879-1883) is full of racial and geographical flavor, with plot enough to prevent the mass from degenerating into mere scientific or impressionistic description. A little later came Miss M. N. Murfree (Charles Egbert Craddock) and her tales of the Tennessee mountaineers, of which the collection called *In the Tennessee Mountains* (1884) contains some of the best. These stories are rich with the melancholy of a wild and forgotten country, but they lack form. Too often she depends, as Harte never does, and Cable seldom, upon dialect, peculiarity of scene or circumstance for success. This will not do in narrative, which, whatever else it accomplishes, must tell a story. Virginia followed, with Thomas Nelson Page's *In Ole Virginia* (1887), the Maine coast in Sarah Orne Jewett's powerful *A Native of Winby* (1893 col.), and many other stories, the hill towns of New England in Mrs. Wilkins-Freeman's *A Humble Romance* (1887 col.) and *A New England Nun* (1891 col.); Western Pennsylvania in Margaret Deland's *Old Chester Tales* (1898). And a general exploitation of dialects, customs, scenery, the rags, tatters, waifs, strays, and left-behinds of civilization generally, accompanied these finer examples.

Three of the women in this list are particularly interesting, for their stories indicate the especial lines of development followed by the really valuable among our thousands of local-color stories in the decades just before the close of the nineteenth century. Miss Jewett was not content with the superficies of the local life she studied. In *The Country of the Pointed Firs* (1896), and like stories, she tried to establish a true relationship between the rocky country she loved and its weathered inhabitants. Mrs. Wilkins-Freeman, whose pen is far more skilful, goes further. With her, the setting is interesting only for its effect upon the dwellers of her hill country. She deals with the subtle influence of a hard, unlovely life upon temperament; she is a conscientious realist, who constructs her little stories as carefully as Maupassant himself. In fact, in spite of the difference in moral angle, she writes more like Maupassant than does any other American author. With her, the local-color story in English reaches its highest point of finesse; but loses in vividness, and sometimes in force. Margaret Deland is almost no local colorist at all in the narrow sense of the word, for her *Old Chester Tales* could be shifted into any rural community in the East with no damage to their essential values. Personality is what she seeks, and the careful details of her rural neighborhood merely explain the peculiar nature of her characters, and insure the reality of her work.

One wonders, indeed, whether local color is not, after all, a misnomer for this school; whether its true art is not to be found in the study of the intricate relationship between man's character and environment, and whether the use of peculiar circumstances of some unusual location ought not to be simply a contributory means which adds interest and truth to the story. Certainly this characterization fits the leaders whose work we have just described. And the magazines of this epoch at the end of the nineteenth century also lend assurance to this theory. The many writers (most of them women) whose stock-in-trade was no more than a description of unfamiliar peoples and localities, made no excellent contribution to our fiction, nor has their vogue as individuals lasted. For a while they feminized some of our standard magazines. Fancying that local color was valuable, whether attached to a real story or not, they exalted the weakest element of narrative, setting, at the expense of character and plot; with the result that the public have wearied of them. They degraded the local-color story into a descriptive sketch.

Thus the story of localities declined from the interests of good narrative; indeed, the writers who practise it in the new developments which our times have brought about have not yet escaped from the fallacy that facts or impressions alone can make fiction. Nevertheless, in the hands of the real artists of the school, it has been responsible for some of our best and our most characteristic short stories. Furthermore, the feeling for local color gave to our fiction, as it has given to others, an invaluable conscientiousness in the use of setting. And this, properly controlled, properly used, may raise the short story or the novel in the next great creative period to a higher artistic level than has hitherto been reached.

XIII

THE DEEPENING OF THE SHORT STORY. HENRY JAMES

So far we have been busy chiefly with the broadening of the field of the American short story, although naturally work like that of Mrs. Wilkins-Freeman must also make it reach deeper into human nature and experience. But now we turn specifically to an earlier deepening of its activities, conducted by one of the master-minds of English fiction, who has been, and is, influential to a degree hardly yet to be estimated.

As early as Harte and Aldrich, Henry James had begun the practice of the short story, but the beginning of his most characteristic work is to be placed in the decade 1870-1880. One of these early stories was *The Madonna of the Future* (1873). An American painter, resident in Florence and optimistic to a degree, believes that it is not too late to paint a great Madonna. But his ideal of what that Madonna should be is eternally in advance of his powers of execution. His chosen model grows old and corrupt; he himself grows old and incapable; while his idea flowers beyond all powers of realization, until, when the famous canvas at last is seen, it is still bare.

This is but one of many experiments in the subtleties of human nature which, since those early days, Henry James has been conducting. It illustrates admirably the direction down and in towards the utmost depths of subjectivity which he has given to the short story. The brief unity of the short tale is made to express the striking incident, the significant phase of the inner, as before of the outer, life. But *The Madonna* is only an example. In later stories he has plunged far deeper, and, to borrow the psychologist's term, since with James we are never far from psychology, he has entered into a surprising variety of mental states. There is *Brooksmith* (1891), which skilfully manipulates the mind of the perfect servant, who is lost when he loses his master; an unpromising subject, surely, until, by James's aid, you discover the fold upon fold of subtlety which go to make up the gradation of that experience. There is *The Turn of the Screw* (1898), a study of intangible, loathly horror, whose theme is the slow corrupting of children's minds. There is the pathetic, but more pleasant, *The Real Thing* (1893), in which the essential principle of aristocracy, apart from all supporting circumstances of wealth and position, is discovered, mounted on a slide, and projected upon the screen of the short story.

That many of James's stories are over-subtle there is no denying, and from an over-subtlety of thought may arise the obscurity of style which often is urged against them. However, this fault, for fault it sometimes is, may be quite as properly charged to this author's evident fondness for minutely accurate statement. It has been said by Mr. James himself that the later stories, where complexity of style is most frequent, have all been dictated, and this would confirm the latter hypothesis, for qualifications of statement which make at the same time for accuracy and complexity come easily from the tongue. In any case, that the genius of this great writer too often plays with his unusual intellectual power, as a skilful swordsman might play with his rapier in the midst of the duello, is clear. Sometimes, at the close of a story, one has the sensation which properly belongs after an experiment in physics. And yet, in the considerable body of short stories which Mr. James has given us, there is a marvelous collection of experiences, sensations, moods, and reactions, which never found their way into fiction before. It is possible that some of them never have existed, nor ever will exist for the average man of our half-intellectualized civilization. But this does not invalidate the insight, or the foresight, of this artist in psychological research; nor does it detract from the great and only half-admitted influence of this work upon later fiction, and especially upon the later short story.

It is very interesting to compare the work of Henry James with that of Hawthorne, that other American explorer of the inner experience, for in so doing one sees more clearly the place which the later writer must be assigned in the development of our short story. Both men work with situations. It is an infinitely delicate, infinitely refined situation which Mr. James uses as a kind of frame upon which he stretches the minds he is about to dissect. Suppose evil influences could be exerted after death by evil advisers; suppose they should be exerted upon the tender minds of children. There is the frame of *The Turn of the Screw*. Suppose a butler in the household of a gentleman who has created by his personal attainments a notable salon, should become dependent upon the society he served there. If that society should dissolve with his master's death, what effect upon him? That is the central situation of *Brooksmith*. One sees that, except in the use of such unifying situations, there is no resemblance to the method of Hawthorne. Hawthorne, indeed, was a moralist who began with a preoccupation—the moral he intended to inculcate. James is an artist in research who studies what he *finds* in the brain, or in the soul, or—more rarely—in the heart. He advanced the short story into new fields much as the scientist has advanced chemical analysis, or microscopic determination. He gave it a trend towards minute specialization, and the exact expression of our subjectivity, quite in keeping with the characteristic interests of the end of the nineteenth century.

Thus the deepening and broadening of the short story was well established by the mid-Eighties. The next development was across the water.

XIV

THE SHORT STORY IN ENGLAND. ROBERT LOUIS STEVENSON

THE ambiguity of the term "short story" becomes especially troublesome when one begins to consider the English fiction of the end of the nineteenth century. If it is to be interpreted to cover all short narrative, many stories clamor for attention. There are the short tales of Meredith and Hardy, the Scotch sketches of Barrie, and innumerable tales and novelettes of a like description. But most of this fiction is in closer relationship to the novel than to the short story whose development in America we have been tracing. Much of it, too, is inferior to other work by the same authors. Little of it is interesting as an attempt to do in short narrative what could not be done in long. If, however, we somewhat arbitrarily elect to study the especial and distinctive short story which the Americans had developed for themselves, and which Americans were using with full consciousness that they had a special tool for special purposes, then the atmosphere lightens. There are only a few English writers of the nineteenth, and, indeed, of the twentieth, centuries who have done notably well with the highly unified, impressionistic short story. All show American influence. Two—the greatest—return this influence with interest. These two, Stevenson and Kipling, should be placed beside Poe, Hawthorne, Harte, and James.

Stevenson began his career as a romancer with a short story, and continued to turn to the short story again and again. He seems to have expected little reputation from these efforts in a supposedly minor art, and, always excepting the success of *Dr. Jekyll and Mr. Hyde,* he got little. But as time goes on the best of these stories, *A Lodging for the Night* (1877), *The Sire de Malétroit's Door* (1878), *Will o' the Mill* (1878), *The Merry Men* (1882), *Markheim* (1885), and *Dr. Jekyll* (1886), which, for all its length, is a short story, bulk more and more among his work. And rightly.

Two general characteristics are especially striking in these stories: the hearty, picturesque romance; and the moral analysis which is the core of each story. In *A Lodging for the Night,* Villon, the poet-rascal, assists at a murder, flies through the snowy streets of medieval Paris, then argues until daybreak with a feudal gentleman over the difference between thieving and war. In setting, incident, and spirit, the story is alive with genuine romance; and a moral situation—the warrior who does great ill nobly, confronted with the thief who does small ill meanly—holds together the plot.

Moralized romance! No one had done that successfully in the short story since Hawthorne. And, indeed, the more one considers Stevenson in this department of his manifold activities the more he appears to be a more artful, less puritanical Hawthorne. The "shorter catechist" whom Henley detected in him, found his opportunity in the short story. *Markheim* and *Dr. Jekyll* are wonderfully picturesque studies of the quality of evil; *Will o' the Mill* an exquisite presentation of the soul that chose the passive voice in life; even the vividly romantic *Sire de Malétroit's Door* hinges upon the question, should a man marry to save his neck? They are more finished than Hawthorne's tales; they are much less didactic, for this lover of things French never made the error of preaching unduly in a work of art. They are also less dogmatic, and, perhaps for that reason, less intense. Hawthorne came before Darwinism—he belongs to the positive thinkers who saw clearly the duty of man and announced it with conviction. He belongs with Carlyle. Stevenson, who came after the triumph of the theory of evolution, is less certain in his views. He is more empirical and, therefore, more tolerant; he puts more emphasis upon a worthy life, and less upon moral law. But, in spite of these great differences, of which the last is highly significant, the resemblance is striking. Both men inquire into the moral nature of man, and turn the results into romance. This resemblance is not accidental. Stevenson was a close student of Hawthorne, particularly in his early years. It is important, however, only in this respect, that it links this first English writer of the new short story to the American line, and gives a comparison which is useful in appreciating his work. Stevenson can well afford the luxury of a source; he has originality enough of his own.

He has originality enough and to spare, for, after all, his philosophy of moral optimism is very much his own; and so is his romantic atmosphere, which has a beautiful reality (a very different thing from a beautiful realism) that makes it more stimulating to the imagination than the work of any recent writer in prose; and so are his characters, which include at least two types, the man obsessed by evil, and the weak man possessed of a strong idealism, that are distinct contributions to fiction. And in style, too, Stevenson did a new thing in the short story. His structure is careful, but upon his style he lavished all his energies. Perhaps it will appear a little Euphuistic when another generation begins to read; and yet no garment could better fit the romantic dignity of his subjects. The symbolic world which lies below Will's mountain pass; Markheim's impassioned pleading for his love of good; the noble simplicities of the ancient warrior of Brisetout—all these the beautiful rhythms of Stevenson set forth with that admirable expressiveness which will, perhaps, be reckoned as the greatest virtue he possessed.

None of these things have powerfully influenced the contemporary short story. Romance had its swing and (disguised as realism) is having another, but it is the romance which Kipling fathered. The psychological analysis which owed so much to Henry James has been more interesting to the writer of our generation than the moral analysis of Stevenson. His style has proved too fine, or too difficult, for the needs of the current stories. Indeed, save in the pure romance of adventure, he has been a real influence only upon the aristocrats of letters—his hand has scarcely touched those factories for the short story where are produced the narratives for the popular magazines. But this does not affect his absolute value; and whether he be regarded as a master of the short story of situation, or as the refiner and beautifier of an art too often practised in slovenliness and haste, that value is very great. A reader must feel renewed respect for the capabilities of short narrative when he finishes his Stevenson.

XV

THE SHORT STORY IN ENGLAND. RUDYARD KIPLING

THE most influential and, in many respects, the greatest of modern writers of the short story has been Rudyard Kipling. In his work, its greatest excellences and its worst tendencies are alike fitly and fully displayed.

It was about 1890 that Kipling's Indian fame broadened into an English and an American celebrity. *Plain Tales from the Hills* (1888), stories written with a sprightly, sometimes a sensational vividness, and dealing with the novel and fascinating contrasts of Indian life, gave him a reputation which he has maintained with far better work. These stories were successful because they were *not* plain. The young Kipling had studied Bret Harte to advantage. The sharp contrasts in the life of Harte's Forty-Niners had not been uninfluential in awakening a consciousness of the "story value" of the still sharper contrasts of Anglo-India. Like Harte, he was a journalist, but with the journalist's command, "be striking; be interesting," far more strong upon him. And in place of Harte's mid-Victorian sentimentality he was filled full of romantic enthusiasm for primitive vigor, and the life of the emotions and the instincts. In a rapid succession of such narratives as *The Man Who Would Be King* (1888), *On Greenhow Hill* (1890), *Without Benefit of Clergy* (1890), Kipling established himself as the master of something vivid and new in the art of local color. Then, with *The Jungle Books* (1894-1895), he entered a world new to romance, and gave us India and the Primitive Emotion by novel and infinitely stirring means.

It is easy now to see what this early Kipling stood for.

He was the apostle of a new romanticism. It was a romanticism of the present instead of the past. For the medieval knight or the eighteenth-century Jacobite he substituted the Englishman, bewildered but omnipotent in the mysterious Orient. For the romantic appeal of history he substituted the equally romantic appeal of vivid local color. Instead of reacting against contemporary impulses, he combined with them, exalting English virility and English self-control, and turning the land hunger of the late nineteenth century into sheer romance. Stevenson was just showing how strong and how enduring was the taste for the romantic story. But Kipling went much further; for by giving to his characters, to his plots, to his scenes, the air of a vivid and current realism, he seized upon the imagination of a great class who, being neither children nor people of literary sensibility, were not easily affected by literary romance. And this is one reason why his influence upon the taste of this English-reading generation has been almost beyond measure.

His means—if we disregard his verse—was the short story, which he took as the Americans, especially as Bret Harte, had left it: a highly unified narrative, made up usually of a striking situation, and driving towards one vivid impression as the result of the whole. This short story was an admirable instrument, unquestionably the best instrument for the work he had to do; but he exaggerated both its merits and its defects. His characters are always immensely striking people: freebooters, exiles, heroic drummer-boys, black panthers, adepts, express engines; their actions are vivid and unusual: a dash for a crown, a love affair with an elephant, the war of the jungle upon man; and the setting is flashed upon the inward eye with all the power of a master of the specific word. Journalism—the gospel of the interesting—is mighty in them, and with admirable effect. With bad effects also; especially upon the numerous imitators who have filled the magazines for twenty years. For journalism means emphasis, and emphasis applied without discrimination leads to one long scream for attention which pains the judicious ear and wearies even the lover of sensationalism. In Kipling's earliest stories, notably in those of the *Plain Tales from the Hills,* where his observation was still immature, and his materials thin, this insistence upon the emphatic leads to a smartness of diction which may be compared to the kind of dressing called "loud." In later and stronger stories it is only of a lack of restraint that one complains—of unnecessary emphasis upon virility, vulgarity, upon all the showy attributes. Read *Pride and Prejudice* before *The Strange Ride of Morrowbie Jukes,* and form the criticism for yourself.

Thus, in his pursuit of a contemporary romance, Kipling journalized the short story. He opened the way for those who have vulgarized it, he is responsible for an infinite amount of superlative high color and extreme action in current fiction; but his service is not to be judged by its faults. The impressionistic short story is clearly an issue of the movement which produced modern journalism; it is part of the modern attempt to get at the truth and get at it quickly. The short story and journalism have grown up together; America among English-speaking nations has been most influential for good and evil upon both. Kipling, whose first inspiration was American, who applied more fully than ever before the methods of one art to the other, was following a true instinct; and our contemporary literature, if it might be more dignified, would be less rich without the result.

In journalizing the short story, Kipling raised one kind

of journalism to the level of literature. This is the reason for his success and the chief attribute of his genius. The wearing qualities of his frontier-stories, and the permanent fascination of his *Jungle-Books* bear witness to this achievement; but it is the later work of Kipling which best illustrates it. There is no sharp division, as some critics would have us believe, between Kipling's earlier and his later periods. The difference lies only in a maturing, a chastening, and a logical development of tendencies already present; with a natural change of subject. Kipling is a greater man than Harte, who worked the California soil after the gold was exhausted. The development has been along several lines, and in every instance the instinct of journalism is manifest. Problems at issue, questions of the day interest Kipling; he has turned to fact-crammed narratives of the "special-article" type, as in *The Army of a Dream,* or the anti-socialistic allegory, *The Mother-Hive.* In these instances the modern journalist's call to preach has been unfortunate, for in such work he has subordinated art, just as in his over-emphatic days he marred it. But in the midst of the new volumes, *Traffics and Discoveries, Actions and Reactions,* come stories of soldiers, of natives, of machines, which exhibit all his old craftsmanship; and, more significantly, with them other tales that reveal the journalist upon a new track. This seeker after the interesting has heard the call of modern mysticism, and begun to delve. He has entered the psychological country of Henry James, and has told of his discoveries in a more interesting fashion. *The Brushwood Boy* (1895), *They* (1904), *An Habitation Enforced* (1905), are thus far the masterpieces of this endeavor. In the first, Kipling writes of dreams come true. *The Brushwood Boy* takes the imaginative sentiment of a young soldier, and makes a story of that; not by analysis, but through a delicate, difficult history of dreams, where this thoroughly healthy person meets his childish fancy, Annieanlouise, and rides with her down the Thirty-Mile Ride, until, in the daytime and awake, he meets her in the flesh. *They* is that incomparable tale of the blind and childless woman whose love brings back the souls of dead children: a story so moving, so delicate, so subtly fine, as to make ridiculous the criticism which disposes of Kipling as the apostle of the primitive, the strenuous, and the loud. *An Habitation Enforced* does not dip into the supernormal, but it probes no less into the human spirit. The grip of the land upon its owners is its theme; more especially the grip of old land rich in human rights and wrongs upon the newcomer, who thinks that he has purchased only so many English acres with his price. It is all the more interesting because it represents, with unusual sympathy, what an Englishman might call the Colonial point of view. Journalism seems at a far remove from these excellent stories. Not so; it is a prime factor in their success. Other men have entered these particular borderlands before; none have made them so realizable, so concrete. Kipling's journalistic instinct for what, in such subtle matters, the reader can grasp and feel, has helped him to write the most interesting report.

Again, there is imaginative history, the last field in which Kipling's genius has wandered. *Puck of Pook's Hill* (1906), *Rewards and Fairies* (1910), are, in the language of journalism, interviews with England's dead. The British captain of Roman legionaries tells the children of the defense of the great wall; Queen Elizabeth strolls and talks in their grove; the man of the stone age recounts his sacrifice for cold iron; and Puck, the super-reporter, manages each interview with veteran skill.

Journalism in the service of literature I call this—and if good journalism, so much the better literature.

We are fortunate to have had our Kipling; and to have him, for these later stories promise rare achievements to come. The journalizing of the short story which he stands for has had an unfortunate effect; it has given rise to a school of magazine writers to whom vividness and immediate interest are the whole of art. But it was a logical, an inevitable development; and must run its course. Just at present the conservative reader is appalled by the avalanche of cheap and easy stories of the Kipling kind. But neither the thousand machine-made imitations, nor the imperfect vessels from the master's wheel, impair the value of the perfect vase. We may disagree with Kiplingism, and deplore the Kiplingesque in literature, but only those who hate the romantic in any form will cry down the type romanticist of the turn of the century.

Finally, Kipling is the most American of all English writers; and his stories belong in everything but the accident of subject-matter to the tradition of the American short story.

XVI

THE CONTEMPORARY SHORT STORY

THE great authority of Stevenson and Kipling has not prevented the contemporary short story from being strongly American in type; and when the debt of these two writers to Hawthorne, to James, and to Harte is properly weighed, this is not surprising. Furthermore, while it is true that good short stories are being written in England, notably by Locke, by Merrick, and by Doyle, nevertheless, if we except Kipling in general, and Doyle in the detective story, and remember that Conrad and Hewlett have become novelists, it will probably be admitted that greater merit as well as greater quantity are prevailingly to be found upon this side of the water. The American short story is usually better than the English, as the English novel is usually better than the American. A superficial cause may be found in the popularity of the illustrated magazine in America, with the opportunity it offers to the writer of the short story. But the real causes lie deeper, in temperament, in environment, in taste, and in the tradition which I have endeavored to follow in these pages.

To attempt anything like a detailed criticism, or even a classification, of modern writers of the short story is beyond the scope of this brief survey, and the powers of the writer. The short story of 1912 must endure time's sifting. And yet some characteristics of contemporary work cannot escape observation, although they may be easily misunderstood.

The form established by the nineteenth century does not seem to be materially changing. Thanks to magazine requirements, American stories have become in general shorter, their mechanism more obvious. In England, two admirable writers were for a time apostles of a freer, broader handling of the short-story idea, Maurice Hewlett, with his charming *Little Novels of Italy* (1899), and Joseph Conrad in his memorable *Youth* (1902). American story-tellers seem to be binding themselves more and more strictly to a rigorous technique. In subject, and, so to speak, in mood, there has been a little more alteration. And yet, in comparison with the new English authors, Wells, Bennett, and Galsworthy, writers of short stories have been strangely conservative. The romantic story of the brusque and adventurous variety, which Kipling made popular, has not lost its vogue, as the success of such writers as Owen Wister, Jack London, Gouverneur Morris, and R. H. Davis proves. The psychological narrative of Henry James has become, with Miss Wharton, a powerful instrument for the analysis of American individuality. And the tendency towards mysticism which Kipling illustrated has certainly not abated. The story with a quip to it, and real and humorous life for a subject, fills our magazines, and has found at least one master in the late O. Henry. These categories present nothing new; but in the contemporary representative of the local-color story there is, perhaps, a novelty. The new local impressionist takes his material not from regions, but from races and classes, and his point of view is more social than psychological. Great quantities of our short stories deal with the immigrant: the Jew, the Pole, or the Japanese. Others take an industrial instead of a racial class, and depict life in the steel mills, the mines, or the wheat fields. A vivid description of the peculiarities of the chosen class distinguishes these stories, and it is here that the vitality of local color shows itself. But there is also a social consciousness (very different from the individualistic self-consciousness of Kipling's stories and Harte's), which relates this work to some of the prevailing tendencies of the times, and suggests the "social conscience" of the new English novel. Often, as in the light sketches of O. Henry and Montague Glass, only humorous capital is made of the class characteristics that give the tale its flavor; but again, for example in some of the narratives of the "muck-raking" school, it would seem that local color has cut loose from the romantic movement which inspired it, and become a means for an imaginative study of our social disorders. It is the new journalized magazine which has encouraged these stories, and, since they must partake of the character of news, it is not surprising to find them more vigorous than artistic.

The short story is certainly in danger from its popularity. That, and especially its adoption by the newspapers, and the illustrated newspapers which we still call magazines, is unquestionably vulgarizing the product. There is a premium upon all that is or can be made journalistic; and the result is a lack of style, which means usually lack of thought, and, worse still, a cheapness and unsubstantiality in the materials out of which the stories are made. What can be expected when they are written for publications which often live but the space between press and dust-bin! And yet only a literary snob could be distressed by these conditions. In some of our weeklies, the short narratives have four times the circulation a Waverley novel could command! Millions want short stories; no talent could supply literary short stories for this clamoring multitude, even if it wanted them. Literature must be bent to its uses, and the demerits of the many need not trouble us if there is merit in a few.

Unfortunately, the few seem to be governed by critical standards better adapted to the many. If one may judge by the current magazines, stories must be respectable, even when vulgar; must end happily; must lend themselves to illustration; must appeal to the average woman; should contain a humorous personality (which will do instead of a plot): restrictions that are not good for art. With a few exceptions, serious work is not given a free hand—except in the humorous story, where the author may study man or woman as intensely as he likes! Triviality may not be preferred—but the evidence points in the opposite direction. Yet the short story has been raised into literature only in those fortunate times when skill, or the circumstances of the moment, have given its slight fabric a serious purpose, a worthy substance, or consummate art. It can be light, it can be graceful, it can be amusing, it can be airy. But triviality kills it.

The short story is also in danger from a change in taste;—not a change on the part of the multitude of readers, for to that it would respond; but a change of taste in the writers who really count. If, as H. G. Wells, brilliant writer of both short stories and novels, has recently said, the social changes which characterize this arc of the century are so truly societal as to require the broad sweep of the novel to record them, then, indeed, the ever moving tide of vital literary energy may take a new direction, and swing its main currents away from the short story through which it has flowed. This is speculation merely; but something like it happened in the sixteenth century, and again at the turn of the nineteenth, when the didactic short narrative of the periodicals disappeared.

But prophesying is poor work. It is better to stick to facts, and to point out what seems to be undeniably true, that it is far easier to find masterpieces of the short story in the half-century before 1900 than in the twelve years after that date; and that the proportion of memorable short stories in the past ten years seems utterly and ridiculously out of keeping with the whole number produced. When the dust settles we may think differently. It may then appear that the vast amount of cheap stuff has blinded us to the relative importance of Kipling's rare experiments in psychic romance; of Miss Wharton's character analysis; of the gems of local color which Mrs. Wilkins-Freeman, Mrs. Deland, and others have recently given us. We must always fight against the prejudice (by no means dead, though now subterranean) against fiction; and remember that a perfect short story, because it *is* a short story, will be strangely undervalued in comparison with artistically second-rate essay, drama, or verse. Nevertheless, it is a fair conclusion that unless new masters arise in the fields of journalism whither we are trending, art will not be so well served by the short story in the immediate future as in the past.

THE PARDONERS TALE *

BY GEOFFREY CHAUCER

Here biginneth the Pardoners Tale.

IN Flaundres whylom was a companye
Of yonge folk, that haunteden folye,
As ryot, hasard, stewes, and tavernes,
Wher-as, with harpes, lutes, and gitermes, 5
They daunce and pleye at dees bothe day and night,
And ete also and drinken over hir might.

. . . . . .

THISE ryotoures three, of whiche I telle,
Longe erst er pryme rong of any belle,
Were set hem in a taverne for to drinke; 10
And as they satte, they herde a belle clinke
Biforn a cors, was caried to his grave;
That oon of hem gan callen to his knave,
'Go bet,' quod he, 'and axe redily,
What cors is this that passeth heer forby; 15
And look that thou reporte his name wel.'
'Sir,' quod this boy, 'it nedeth never-a-del.
It was me told, er ye cam heer, two houres;
He was, pardee, an old felawe of youres;

* GEOFFREY CHAUCER (?1340-1400), writer of this story, was the chief story-teller of the fourteenth century in England. His *Canterbury Tales,* from which this narrative is taken, were probably composed in the years after 1380. The plot of *The Pardoner's Tale* came ultimately from the Orient. See also pp. 3-12.

And sodeynly he was y-slayn to-night,
For-dronke, as he sat on his bench upright;
Ther cam a privee theef, men clepeth Deeth,
That in this contree al the peple sleeth,
5 And with his spere he smoot his herte a-two,
And wente his wey with-outen wordes mo.
He hath a thousand slayn this pestilence:
And, maister, er ye come in his presence,
Me thinketh that it were necessarie
10 For to be war of swich an adversarie:
Beth redy for to mete him evermore.
Thus taughte me my dame, I sey na-more.'
'By seinte Marie,' seyde this taverner,
'The child seith sooth, for he hath slayn this yeer,
15 Henne over a myle, with-in a greet village,
Both man and womman, child and hyne, and page.
I trowe his habitacioun be there;
To been avysed greet wisdom it were,
Er that he dide a man a dishonour.'
20 'Ye, goddes armes,' quod this ryotour,
'Is it swich peril with him for to mete?
I shal him seke by wey and eek by strete,
I make avow to goddes digne bones!
Herkneth, felawes, we three been al ones;
25 Lat ech of us holde up his hond til other,
And ech of us bicomen otheres brother,
And we wol sleen this false traytour Deeth;
He shal be slayn, which that so many sleeth,
By goddes dignitee, er it be night.'
30 Togidres han thise three her trouthes plight,
To live and dyen ech of hem for other,
As though he were his owene y-boren brother.
And up they sterte all dronken, in this rage,
And forth they goon towardes that village,

Of which the taverner had spoke biforn,
And many a grisly ooth than han they sworn,
And Cristes blessed body they to-rente—
'Deeth shal be deed, if that they may him hente.'
Whan they han goon nat fully half a myle, 5
Right as they wolde han troden over a style,
An old man and a povre with hem mette.
This olde man ful mekely hem grette,
And seyde thus, 'now, lordes, god yow see!'
The proudest of thise ryotoures three 10
Answerde agayn, 'what? carl, with sory grace,
Why artow al forwrapped save thy face?
Why livestow so longe in so greet age?'
This olde man gan loke in his visage,
And seyde thus, 'for I ne can nat finde 15
A man, though that I walked in-to Inde,
Neither in citee nor in no village,
That wolde chaunge his youthe for myn age;
And therfore moot I han myn age stille,
As longe time as it is goddes wille. 20
Ne deeth, allas! ne wol nat han my lyf;
Thus walke I, lyk a restelees caityf,
And on the ground, which is my modres gate,
I knokke with my staf, bothe erly and late,
And seye, "leve moder, leet me in! 25
Lo, how I vanish, flesh, and blood, and skin!
Allas! whan shul my bones been at reste?
Moder, with yow wolde I chaunge my cheste,
That in my chambre longe tyme hath be,
Ye! for an heyre clout to wrappe me!" 30
But yet to me she wol nat do that grace,
For which ful pale and welked is my face.
But, sirs, to yow it is no curteisye
To speken to an old man vileinye,

But he trespasse in worde, or elles in dede.
In holy writ ye may your-self wel rede,
"Agayns an old man, hoor upon his heed,
Ye sholde aryse;" wherfor I yeve yow reed,
5 Ne dooth un-to an old man noon harm now,
Na-more than ye wolde men dide to yow
In age, if that ye so longe abyde;
And god be with yow, wher ye go or ryde.
I moot go thider as I have to go.'
10 'Nay, olde cherl, by god, thou shalt nat so,'
Seyde this other hasardour anon;
'Thou partest nat so lightly, by seint John!
Thou spak right now of thilke traitour Deeth,
That in this contree alle our frendes sleeth.
15 Have heer my trouthe, as thou art his aspye,
Tel wher he is, or thou shalt it abye,
By god, and by the holy sacrament!
For soothly thou art oon of his assent,
To sleen us yonge folk, thou false theef!'
20 'Now, sirs,' quod he, 'if that yow be so leef
To finde Deeth, turne up this croked wey,
For in that grove I lafte him, by my fey,
Under a tree, and ther he wol abyde;
Nat for your boost he wol him no-thing hyde.
25 See ye that ook? right ther ye shul him finde.
God save yow, that boghte agayn mankinde,
And yow amende!'—thus seyde this olde man,
And everich of thise ryotoures ran,
Til he cam to that tree, and ther they founde
30 Of florins fyne of golde y-coyned rounde
Wel ny an eighte busshels, as hem thoughte.
No lenger thanne after Deeth they soughte,
But ech of hem so glad was of that sighte,
For that the florins been so faire and brighte,

That doun they sette hem by this precious hord.
The worste of hem he spake the firste word.
 'Brethren,' quod he, 'tak kepe what I seye;
My wit is greet, though that I bourde and pleye.
This tresor hath fortune un-to us yiven, 5
In mirthe and jolitee our lyf to liven,
And lightly as it comth, so wol we spende.
Ey! goddes precious dignitee! who wende
To-day, that we sholde han so fair a grace?
But mighte this gold be caried fro this place 10
Hoom to myn hous, or elles un-to youres—
For wel ye woot that al this gold is oures—
Than were we in heigh felicitee.
But trewely, by daye it may nat be;
Men wolde seyn that we were theves stronge, 15
And for our owene tresor doon us honge.
This tresor moste y-caried be by nighte
As wysly and as slyly as it mighte.
Wherfore I rede that cut among us alle
Be drawe, and lat see wher the cut wol falle; 20
And he that hath the cut with herte blythe
Shal renne to the toune, and that ful swythe,
And bringe us breed and wyn ful prively.
And two of us shul kepen subtilly
This tresor wel; and, if he wol nat tarie, 25
Whan it is night, we wol this tresor carie
By oon assent, wher-as us thinketh best.'
That oon of hem the cut broughte in his fest;
And bad hem drawe, and loke wher it wol falle;
And it fil on the yongeste of hem alle; 30
And forth toward the toun he wente anon.
And al-so sone as that he was gon,
That oon of hem spak thus un-to that other,
'Thou knowest wel thou art my sworne brother,

Thy profit wol I telle thee anon.
Thou woost wel that our felawe is agon;
And heer is gold, and that ful greet plentee,
That shal departed been among us three.
5 But natheles, if I can shape it so
That it departed were among us two,
Hadde I nat doon a freendes torn to thee?'
That other answerde, 'I noot how that may be;
He woot how that the gold is with us tweye,
10 What shal we doon, what shal we to him seye?'
'Shal it be conseil?' seyde the firste shrewe,
'And I shal tellen thee, in wordes fewe,
What we shal doon, and bringe it wel aboute.'
'I graunte,' quod that other, 'out of doute,
15 That, by my trouthe, I wol thee nat biwreye.'
'Now,' quod the firste, 'thou woost wel we be tweye,
And two of us shul strenger be than oon.
Look whan that he is set, and right anoon
Arys, as though thou woldest with him pleye;
20 And I shal ryve him thurgh the sydes tweye
Whyl that thou strogelest with him as in game,
And with thy dagger look thou do the same;
And than shal al this gold departed be,
My dere freend, bitwixen me and thee;
25 Than may we bothe our lustes al fulfille,
And pleye at dees right at our owene wille.'
And thus acorded been thise shrewes tweye
To sleen the thridde, as ye han herd me seye.
This yongest, which that wente un-to the toun,
30 Ful ofte in herte he rolleth up and doun
The beautee of thise florins newe and brighte.
'O lord!' quod he, 'if so were that I mighte
Have al this tresor to my-self allone,
Ther is no man that liveth under the trone

Of god, that sholde live so mery as I!'
And atte laste the feend, our enemy,
Putte in his thought that he shold poyson beye,
With which he mighte sleen his felawes tweye;
For-why the feend fond him in swich lyvinge, 5
That he had leve him to sorwe bringe,
For this was outrely his fulle entente
To sleen hem bothe, and never to repente.
And forth he gooth, no lenger wolde he tarie,
Into the toun, un-to a pothecarie, 10
And preyed him, that he him wolde selle
Som poyson, that he mighte his rattes quelle;
And eek ther was a polcat in his hawe,
That, as he seyde, his capouns hadde y-slawe,
And fayn he wolde wreke him, if he mighte, 15
On vermin, that destroyed him by nighte.
The pothecarie answerde, 'and thou shalt have
A thing that, al-so god my soule save,
In al this world ther nis no creature,
That ete or dronke hath of this confiture 20
Noght but the mountance of a corn of whete,
That he ne shal his lyf anon forlete;
Ye, sterve he shal, and that in lasse whyle
Than thou wolt goon a paas nat but a myle;
This poyson is so strong and violent.' 25
This cursed man hath in his hond y-hent
This poyson in a box, and sith he ran
In-to the nexte strete, un-to a man,
And borwed [of] him large botels three;
And in the two his poyson poured he; 30
The thridde he kepte clene for his drinke.
For al the night he shoop him for to swinke
In caryinge of the gold out of that place.
And whan this ryotour, with sory grace,

Had filled with wyn his grete botels three,
To his felawes agayn repaireth he.
What nedeth it to sermone of it more?
For right as they had cast his deeth bifore,
5 Right so they han him slayn, and that anon.
And whan that this was doon, thus spak that oon,
'Now lat us sitte and drinke, and make us merie,
And afterward we wol his body berie.'
And with that word it happed him, par cas,
10 To take the botel ther the poyson was,
And drank, and yaf his felawe drinke also,
For which anon they storven bothe two.
But, certes, I suppose that Avicen
Wroot never in no canon, ne in no fen,*
15 Mo wonder signes of empoisoning
Than hadde thise wrecches two, er hir ending.
Thus ended been thise homicydes two,
And eek the false empoysoner also.

Here is ended the Pardoners Tale.

* *Fen,* the Arabic name of the sections of Avicenna's Canon.

THE PRIORESSES TALE *

BY GEOFFREY CHAUCER

THER was in Asie, in a greet citee,
Amonges Cristen folk, a Jewerye,
Sustened by a lord of that contree
For foule usure and lucre of vilanye,
Hateful to Crist and to his companye; 5
And thurgh the strete men mighte ryde or wende,
For it was free, and open at either ende.

A litel scole of Cristen folk ther stood
Doun at the ferther ende, in which ther were
Children an heep, y-comen of Cristen blood, 10
That lerned in that scole yeer by yere
Swich maner doctrine as men used there,
This is to seyn, to singen and to rede,
As smale children doon in hir childhede.

Among thise children was a widwes sone, 15
A litel clergeon, seven yeer of age,
That day by day to scole was his wone,
And eek also, wher-as he saugh th'image
Of Cristes moder, hadde he in usage,

* See note to *The Pardoner's Tale*. This story had been told by earlier writers, but never before so well. The piety and the unjust attack upon the Jews are equally characteristic of the Middle Ages. See also pp. 3-12.

As him was taught, to knele adoun and seye
His *Ave Marie,* as he goth by the weye.

Thus hath this widwe hir litel sone y-taught
Our blisful lady, Cristes moder dere,
5 To worshipe ay, and he forgat it naught,
For sely child wol alday sone lere;
But ay, whan I remembre on this matere,
Seint Nicholas stant ever in my presence,
For he so yong to Crist did reverence.

10 This litel child, his litel book lerninge,
As he sat in the scole at his prymer,
He *Alma redemptoris* herde singe,
As children lerned hir antiphoner;
And, as he dorste, he drough him ner and ner,
15 And herkned ay the wordes and the note,
Til he the firste vers coude al by rote.

Noght wiste he what this Latin was to seye,
For he so yong and tendre was of age;
But on a day his felaw gan he preye
20 T'expounden him this song in his langage,
Or telle him why this song was in usage;
This preyde he him to construe and declare
Ful ofte tyme upon his knowes bare.

His felaw, which that elder was than he,
25 Answerde him thus: 'this song, I have herd seye,
Was maked of our blisful lady free,
Hir to salue, and eek hir for to preye
To been our help and socour whan we deye.
I can no more expounde in this matere;
30 I lerne song, I can but smal grammere.'

'And is this song maked in reverence
Of Cristes moder?' seyde this innocent;
'Now certes, I wol do my diligence
To conne it al, er Cristemasse is went;
Though that I for my prymer shal be shent, 5
And shal be beten thryës in an houre,
I wol it conne, our lady for to honoure.'

His felaw taughte him homward prively,
Fro day to day, til he coude it by rote,
And than he song it wel and boldely 10
Fro word to word, acording with the note;
Twyës a day it passed thurgh his throte,
To scoleward and homward whan he wente;
On Cristes moder set was his entente.

As I have seyd, thurgh-out the Jewerye 15
This litel child, as he cam to and fro,
Ful merily than wolde he singe, and crye
O Alma redemptoris ever-mo.
The swetnes hath his herte perced so
Of Cristes moder, that, to hir to preye, 20
He can nat stinte of singing by the weye.

Our firste fo, the serpent Sathanas,
That hath in Jewes herte his waspes nest,
Up swal, and seide, 'O Hebraik peple, allas!
Is this to yow a thing that is honest, 25
That swich a boy shal walken as him lest
In your despyt, and singe of swich sentence,
Which is agayn your lawes reverence?'

Fro thennes forth the Jewes han conspyred
This innocent out of this world to chace; 30
An homicyde ther-to han they hyred,

That in an aley hadde a privee place;
And as the child gan for-by for to pace,
This cursed Jew him hente and heeld him faste,
And kitte his throte, and in a pit him caste.

5 I seye that in a wardrobe they him threwe
Wher-as these Jewes purgen hir entraille.
O cursed folk of Herodes al newe,
What may your yvel entente yow availle?
Mordre wol out, certein, it wol nat faille,
10 And namely ther th'onour of god shal sprede,
The blood out cryeth on your cursed dede.

'O martir, souded to virginitee,
Now maystou singen, folwing ever in oon
The whyte lamb celestial,' quod she,
15 'Of which the grete evangelist, seint John,
In Pathmos wroot, which seith that they that goon
Biforn this lamb, and singe a song al newe,
That never, fleshly, wommen they ne knewe.'

This povre widwe awaiteth al that night
20 After hir litel child, but he cam noght;
For which, as sone as it was dayes light,
With face pale of drede and bisy thoght,
She hath at scole and elles-wher him soght,
Til finally she gan so fer espye
25 That he last seyn was in the Jewerye.

With modres pitee in hir brest enclosed,
She gooth, as she were half out of hir minde,
To every place wher she hath supposed
By lyklihede hir litel child to finde;
30 And ever on Cristes mode meke and kinde

She cryde, and atte laste thus she wroghte,
Among the cursed Jewes she him soghte.

She frayneth and she preyeth pitously
To every Jew that dwelte in thilke place,
To telle hir, if hir child wente oght for-by. 5
They seyde, 'nay'; but Jesu, of his grace,
Yaf in hir thought, inwith a litel space,
That in that place after hir sone she cryde,
Wher he was casten in a pit bisyde.

O grete god, that parfournest thy laude 10
By mouth of innocents, lo heer thy might!
This gemme of chastitee, this emeraude,
And eek of martirdom the ruby bright,
Ther he with throte y-corven lay upright,
He '*Alma redemptoris*' gan to singe 15
So loude, that al the place gan to ringe.

The Cristen folk, that thurgh the strete wente,
In coomen, for to wondre up-on this thing,
And hastily they for the provost sente;
He cam anon with-outen tarying, 20
And herieth Crist that is of heven king,
And eek his moder, honour of mankinde,
And after that, the Jewes leet he binde.

This child with pitous lamentacioun
Up-taken was, singing his song alway; 25
And with honour of greet processioun
They carien him un-to the nexte abbay.
His moder swowning by the bere lay;
Unnethe might the peple that was there
This newe Rachel bringe fro his bere. 30

With torment and with shamful deth echon
This provost dooth thise Jewes for to sterve
That of this mordre wiste, and that anon;
He nolde no swich cursednesse observe.
5 Yvel shal have, that yvel wol deserve.
Therfor with wilde hors he dide hem drawe,
And after that he heng hem by the lawe.

Up-on his bere ay lyth this innocent
Biforn the chief auter, whyl masse laste,
10 And after that, the abbot with his covent
Han sped hem for to burien him ful faste;
And whan they holy water on him caste,
Yet spak this child, whan spreynd was holy water,
And song—'*O Alma redemptoris mater!*'

15 This abbot, which that was an holy man
As monkes been, or elles oghten be,
This yonge child to conjure he bigan,
And seyde, 'o dere child, I halse thee,
In vertu of the holy Trinitee,
20 Tel me what is thy cause for to singe,
Sith that thy throte is cut, to my seminge?'

'My throte is cut un-to my nekke-boon,'
Seyde this child, 'and, as by wey of kinde,
I sholde have deyed, ye, longe tyme agoon,
25 But Jesu Crist, as ye in bokes finde,
Wil that his glorie laste and be in minde;
And, for the worship of his moder dere,
Yet may I singe "*O Alma*" loude and clere.

This welle of mercy, Cristes moder swete,
30 I lovede alwey, as after my conninge;

And whan that I my lyf sholde forlete,
To me she cam, and bad me for to singe
This antem verraily in my deyinge,
As ye han herd, and, whan that I had songe,
Me thoughte, she leyde a greyn up-on my tonge. 5

Wherfor I singe, and singe I moot certeyn
In honour of that blisful mayden free,
Til fro my tonge of-taken is the greyn;
And afterward thus seyde she to me,
"My litel child, now wol I fecche thee 10
Whan that the greyn is fro thy tonge y-take;
Be nat agast, I wol thee nat forsake."'

This holy monk, this abbot, him mene I,
Him tonge out-caughte, and took a-wey the greyn,
And he yaf up the goost ful softely. 15
And whan this abbot had this wonder seyn,
His salte teres trikled doun as reyn,
And gruf he fil al plat up-on the grounde,
And stille he lay as he had been y-bounde.

The covent eek lay on the pavement 20
Weping, and herien Cristes moder dere,
And after that they ryse, and forth ben went,
And toke awey this martir fro his bere,
And in a tombe of marbul-stones clere
Enclosen they his litel body swete; 25
Ther he is now, god leve us for to mete.

O yonge Hugh of Lincoln, slayn also
With cursed Jewes, as it is notable,
For it nis but a litel whyle ago;

Preye eek for us, we sinful folk unstable,
That, of his mercy, god so merciable
On us his grete mercy multiplye,
For reverence of his moder Marye. Amen.

THE VISION OF MIRZA*

BY JOSEPH ADDISON

No. 159. SATURDAY, SEPTEMBER 1. [1711.]

Omnem, quæ nunc obducta tuenti
Mortales hebetat visus tibi, et humida circum
Caligat, nubem eripiam.—VIRG.

WHEN I was at Grand Cairo I picked up several 5
oriental manuscripts, which I have still by me. Among others I met with one entitled "The Visions of Mirzah," which I have read over with great pleasure. I intend to give it to the public when I have no other entertainment for them; and shall begin with the first 10
vision, which I have translated word for word as follows.

"On the fifth day of the moon, which according to the custom of my forefathers I always keep holy, after having washed myself, and offered up my morning devotions, I ascended the high hills of Bagdat, in order to 15
pass the rest of the day in meditation and prayer. As I was here airing myself on the tops of the mountains, I fell into a profound contemplation on the vanity of human life; and passing from one thought to another,

* JOSEPH ADDISON (1672-1719), chief author of *The Spectator,* in which this story appears under date of September 1, 1711, is best remembered for the urbane essays, criticisms, and stories which appeared in that well-known periodical, and as one of the most eminent of the literary men of the reign of Queen Anne. See also pp. 22-26, 30.

'Surely,' said I, 'man is but a shadow and life a dream.' Whilst I was thus musing, I cast my eyes towards the summit of a rock that was not far from me, where I discovered one in the habit of a shepherd, with a musical
5 instrument in his hand. As I looked upon him he applied it to his lips, and began to play upon it. The sound of it was exceeding sweet, and wrought into a variety of tunes that were inexpressibly melodious, and altogether different from any thing I had ever heard.
10 They put me in mind of those heavenly airs that are played to the departed souls of good men upon their first arrival in Paradise, to wear out the impressions of their last agonies, and qualify them for the pleasures of that happy place. My heart melted away in secret
15 raptures.

"I had been often told that the rock before me was the haunt of a genius; and that several had been entertained with music who had passed by it, but never heard that the musician had before made himself visible. When
20 he had raised my thoughts, by those transporting airs which he played, to taste the pleasures of his conversation, as I looked upon him like one astonished, he beckoned to me, and by the waving of his hand directed me to approach the place where he sat. I drew near with that
25 reverence which is due to a superior nature; and as my heart was entirely subdued by the captivating strains I had heard, I fell down at his feet and wept. The genius smiled upon me with a look of compassion and affability that familiarized him to my imagination, and at once
30 dispelled all the fears and apprehensions with which I approached him. He lifted me from the ground, and taking me by the hand, 'Mirzah,' said he, 'I have heard thee in thy soliloquies, follow me.'

"He then led me to the highest pinnacle of the rock,

and placing me on the top of it, 'Cast thy eyes eastward,' said he, 'and tell me what thou seest.' 'I see,' said I, 'a huge valley and a prodigious tide of water rolling through it.' 'The valley that thou seest,' said he, 'is the vale of misery, and the tide of water that thou seest, is 5 part of the great tide of eternity.' 'What is the reason,' said I, 'that the tide I see rises out of a thick mist at one end, and again loses itself in a thick mist at the other?' 'What thou seest,' said he, 'is that portion of eternity which is called time, measured out by the sun, 10 and reaching from the beginning of the world to its consummation. Examine now,' said he, 'this sea that is thus bounded with darkness at both ends, and tell me what thou discoverest in it.' 'I see a bridge,' said I, 'standing in the midst of the tide.' 'The bridge thou 15 seest,' said he, 'is human life; consider it attentively.' Upon a more leisurely survey of it, I found that it consisted of threescore and ten entire arches, with several broken arches, which added to those that were entire, made up the number about an hundred. As I was count- 20 ing the arches the genius told me that this bridge consisted at first of a thousand arches; but that a great flood swept away the rest, and left the bridge in the ruinous condition I now beheld it. 'But tell me further,' said he, 'what thou discoverest on it.' 25

"'I see multitudes of people passing over it,' said I, 'and a black cloud hanging on each end of it.' As I looked more attentively, I saw several of the passengers dropping through the bridge, into the great tide that flowed underneath it; and upon further examination, per- 30 ceived there were innumerable trap-doors that lay concealed in the bridge, which the passengers no sooner trod upon, but they fell through them into the tide and immediately disappeared. These hidden pit-falls were set very

thick at the entrance of the bridge, so that throngs of people no sooner broke through the cloud, but many of them fell into them. They grew thinner towards the middle, but multiplied and lay closer together towards
5 the end of the arches that were entire.

"There were indeed some persons, but their number was very small, that continued a kind of hobbling march on the broken arches, but fell through one after another, being quite tired and spent with so long a walk.

10 "I passed some time in the contemplation of this wonderful structure, and the great variety of objects which it presented. My heart was filled with a deep melancholy to see several dropping unexpectedly in the midst of mirth and jollity, and catching at every thing that stood by
15 them to save themselves. Some were looking up towards the heavens in a thoughtful posture, and in the midst of a speculation stumbled and fell out of sight. Multitudes were very busy in the pursuit of bubbles that glittered in their eyes and danced before them, but often when
20 they thought themselves within the reach of them, their footing failed and down they sunk. In this confusion of objects, I observed some with scimitars in their hands, and others with urinals, who ran to and fro upon the bridge, thrusting several persons on trap-doors which
25 did not seem to lie in their way, and which they might have escaped, had they not been thus forced upon them.

"The genius seeing me indulge myself in this melancholy prospect, told me I had dwelt long enough upon it: 'Take thine eyes off the bridge,' said he, 'and tell me if
30 thou seest any thing thou dost not comprehend.' Upon looking up, 'What mean,' said I, 'those great flights of birds that are perpetually hovering about the bridge, and settling upon it from time to time? I see vultures, harpies, ravens, cormorants; and among many other

feathered creatures several little winged boys, that perch in great numbers upon the middle arches.' 'These,' said the genius, 'are envy, avarice, superstition, despair, love, with the like cares and passions that infest human life.'

"I here fetched a deep sigh; 'Alas,' said I, 'man was 5 made in vain! how is he given away to misery and mortality! tortured in life, and swallowed up in death!' The genius, being moved with compassion towards me, bid me quit so uncomfortable a prospect. 'Look no more,' said he, 'on man in the first stage of his existence, in his 10 setting out for eternity; but cast thine eye on that thick mist into which the tide bears the several generations of mortals that fall into it.' I directed my sight as I was ordered, and (whether or no the good genius strengthened it with any supernatural force, or dissipated part 15 of the mist that was before too thick for the eye to penetrate) I saw the valley opening at the further end, and spreading forth into an immense ocean, that had a huge rock of adamant running through the midst of it, and dividing it into two equal parts. The clouds still rested 20 on one half of it, insomuch that I could discover nothing in it: but the other appeared to me a vast ocean planted with innumerable islands, that were covered with fruits and flowers, and interwoven with a thousand little shining seas that ran among them. I could see persons 25 dressed in glorious habits with garlands upon their heads, passing among the trees, lying down by the sides of fountains, or resting on beds of flowers; and could hear a confused harmony of singing birds, falling waters, human voices, and musical instruments. Gladness grew in me 30 upon the discovery of so delightful a scene. I wished for the wings of an eagle, that I might fly away to those happy seats; but the genius told me there was no passage to them, except through the gates of death that I saw

opening every moment upon the bridge. 'The islands,' said he, 'that lie so fresh and green before thee, and with which the whole face of the ocean appears spotted as far as thou canst see, are more in number than the sands
5 on the sea-shore; there are myriads of islands behind those which thou here discoverest, reaching further than thine eye or even thine imagination can extend itself. These are the mansions of good men after death, who according to the degree and kinds of virtue in which they
10 excelled, are distributed among these several islands, which abound with pleasures of different kinds and degrees, suitable to the relishes and perfections of those who are settled in them; every island is a paradise accommodated to its respective inhabitants. Are not these, O Mirzah,
15 habitations worth contending for? Does life appear miserable, that gives thee opportunities of earning such a reward? is death to be feared that will convey thee to so happy an existence? Think not man was made in vain, who has such an eternity reserved for him.' I gazed
20 with inexpressible pleasure on these happy islands. At length said I, 'Show me now, I beseech thee, the secrets that lie hid under those dark clouds which cover the ocean on the other side of the rock of adamant.' The genius making me no answer, I turned about to address
25 myself to him a second time, but I found that he had left me; I then turned again to the vision which I had been so long contemplating, but instead of the rolling tide, the arched bridge, and the happy islands, I saw nothing but the long hollow valley of Bagdat, with oxen,
30 sheep, and camels, grazing upon the sides of it."

The end of the first vision of Mirzah.

THE LINGERING EXPECTATION OF AN HEIR *

BY SAMUEL JOHNSON

TUESDAY, NOV. 27, 1750.

Stulte, quid O frustra votis puerilibus optas
Quæ non ulla tulit, fertve, feretve dies.—OVID.

Why thinks the fool, with childish hope, to see
What neither is, nor was, nor e'er shall be? 5
—ELPHINSTON.

TO THE RAMBLER

SIR,

If you feel any of that compassion which you recommend to others, you will not disregard a case which I 10 have reason from observation to believe very common, and which I know by experience to be very miserable. And though the querulous are seldom received with great ardor of kindness, I hope to escape the mortification of finding that my lamentations spread the contagion of 15 impatience, and produce anger rather than tenderness. I write not merely to vent the swelling of my heart, but to inquire by what means I may recover my tranquillity;

* DR. SAMUEL JOHNSON (1709-1784), author of *The Rambler,* a short-lived periodical where this narrative sketch appeared under date of November 27, 1750, composed the first great English dictionary, was eminent in conversation and literary criticism, and has been made eternally famous by Boswell's great biography. See also pp. 22-26.

and shall endeavor at brevity in my narrative, having long known that complaint quickly tires, however elegant or however just.

I was born in a remote county, of a family that boasts 5 alliances with the greatest names in English history, and extends its claims of affinity to the Tudors and Plantagenets. My ancestors by little and little wasted their patrimony, till my father had not enough left for the support of a family, without descending to the cultiva-10 tion of his own grounds, being condemned to pay three sisters the fortunes allotted them by my grandfather, who is suspected to have made his will when he was incapable of adjusting properly the claims of his children, and who, perhaps, without design, enriched his daughters 15 by beggaring his son. My aunts being, at the death of their father, neither young nor beautiful, nor very eminent for softness of behavior, were suffered to live unsolicited, and by accumulating the interest of their portions, grew every day richer and prouder. My father pleased himself with 20 foreseeing that the possessions of those ladies must revert at last to the hereditary estate, and, that his family might lose none of its dignity, resolved to keep me untainted with a lucrative employment: whenever therefore I discovered any inclination to the improvement of my condi-25 tion, my mother never failed to put me in mind of my birth, and charged me to do nothing with which I might be reproached when I should come to my aunts' estate.

In all the perplexities or vexations which want of money brought upon us, it was our constant practice to 30 have recourse to futurity. If any of our neighbors surpassed us in appearance, we went home and contrived an equipage, with which the death of my aunts was to supply us. If any purseproud upstart was deficient in respect, vengeance was referred to the time in which our estate was to be repaired. We registered every act of civility and rudeness, inquired the number of dishes at every feast, and minuted the furniture of every house, that we might, when the hour of affluence should come, be able to eclipse all their splendor, and surpass all their 5 magnificence.

Upon plans of elegance, and schemes of pleasure, the day rose and set, and the year went around unregarded, while we were busied in laying our plantations on ground not yet our own, and deliberating whether the manor- 10 house should be rebuilt or repaired. This was the amusement of our leisure, and the solace of our exigences; we met together only to contrive how our approaching fortune should be enjoyed; for in this our conversation always ended, on whatever subject it began. We had 15 none of the collateral interests, which diversify the life of others with joys and hopes, but had turned our whole attention on one event, which we could neither hasten nor retard, and had no other object of curiosity than the health or sickness of my aunts, of which we were careful 20 to procure very exact and early intelligence.

This visionary opulence for a while soothed our imagination, but afterward fired our wishes, and exasperated our necessities, and my father could not always restrain himself from exclaiming, that no creature had so many 25 lives as a cat and an old maid. At last upon the recovery of his sister from an ague, which she was supposed to have caught by sparing fire, he began to lose his stomach, and four months afterwards sunk into the grave.

My mother, who loved her husband, survived him but 30 a little while, and left me the sole heir of their lands, their schemes, and their wishes. As I had not enlarged my conceptions either by books or conversation, I differed only from my father by the freshness of my cheeks, and the vigor of my step: and, like him, gave way to no thoughts but of enjoying the wealth which my aunts were hoarding.

At length the eldest fell ill. I paid the civilities and
5 compliments which sickness requires with the utmost punctuality. I dreamed every night of escutcheons and white gloves, and inquired every morning at an early hour, whether there were any news of my dear aunt. At last a messenger was sent to inform me that I must
10 come to her without the delay of a moment. I went and heard her last advice, but opening her will, found that she had left her fortune to her second sister.

I hung my head; the youngest sister threatened to be married, and every thing was disappointment and dis-
15 content. I was in danger of losing irreparably one-third of my hopes, and was condemned still to wait for the rest. Of part of my terror I was soon eased; for the youth, whom his relations would have compelled to marry the old lady, after innumerable stipulations, arti-
20 cles, and settlements, ran away with the daughter of his father's groom; and my aunt, upon this conviction of the perfidy of man, resolved never to listen more to amorous addresses.

Ten years longer I dragged the shackles of expecta-
25 tion, without ever suffering a day to pass in which I did not compute how much my chance was improved of being rich to-morrow. At last the second lady died, after a short illness, which yet was long enough to afford her time for the disposal of her estate, which she gave
30 to me after the death of her sister.

I was now relieved from part of my misery; a large fortune, though not in my power, was certain and unalienable; nor was there now any danger that I might at last be frustrated of my hopes by fret of dotage, the flatteries of a chamber-maid, the whispers of a tale-bearer, or the officiousness of a nurse. But my wealth was yet in reversion, my aunt was to be buried before I could emerge to grandeur and pleasure; and there was yet, according to my father's observation, nine lives be- 5 tween me and happiness.

I however lived on, without any clamors of discontent, and comforted myself with considering that all are mortal, and they who are continually decaying, must at last be destroyed. 10

But let no man from this time suffer his felicity to depend on the death of his aunt. The good gentlewoman was very regular in her hours, and simple in her diet; and in walking or sitting still, waking or sleeping, had always in view the preservation of her health. She 15 was subject to no disorder but hypochondriac dejection; by which, without intention, she increased my miseries, for whenever the weather was cloudy, she would take her bed and send me notice that her time was come. I went with all the haste of eagerness, and sometimes re- 20 ceived passionate injunctions to be kind to her maid, and directions how the last offices should be performed; but if before my arrival the sun happened to break out, or the wind to change, I met her at the door, or found her in the garden, bustling and vigilant, with all the tokens 25 of long life.

Sometimes, however, she fell into distempers, and was thrice given over by the doctor, yet she found means of slipping through the gripe of death, and after having tortured me three months at each time with violent alter- 30 nations of hope and fear, came out of her chamber without any other hurt than the loss of flesh, which in a few weeks she recovered by broths and jellies.

As most have sagacity sufficient to guess at the desires

of an heir, it was the constant practice of those who were hoping at second hand, and endeavored to secure my favor against the time when I should be rich, to pay their court, by informing me that my aunt began to droop, that she 5 had lately a bad night, that she coughed feebly, and that she could never climb May hill; or, at least, that the autumn would carry her off. Thus was I flattered in the winter with the piercing winds of March, and in the summer with the fogs of September. But she lived 10 through spring and fall and set heat and cold at defiance, till, after nearly half a century, I buried her on the fourteenth of last June, aged ninety-three years, five months, and six days.

For two months after her death I was rich, and was 15 pleased with that obsequiousness and reverence which wealth instantaneously procures. But this joy is now past, and I have returned again to my old habit of wishing. Being accustomed to give the future full power over my mind, and to start away from the scene before me to some 20 expected enjoyment, I deliver up myself to the tyranny of every desire which fancy suggests, and long for a thousand things which I am unable to procure. Money has much less power than is ascribed to it by those that want it. I had formed schemes which I cannot 25 execute, I had supposed events which do not come to pass, and the rest of my life must pass in craving solicitude, unless you can find some remedy for a mind corrupted with an inveterate disease of wishing, and unable to think on any thing but wants, which reason tells me 30 will never be supplied.

I am, &c.,

CUPIDUS.

WANDERING WILLIE'S TALE *

By SIR WALTER SCOTT

"HONEST folks like me! How do ye ken whether I am honest, or what I am? I may be the deevil himsell for what ye ken, for he has power to come disguised like an angel of light; and, besides, he is a prime fiddler. He played a sonata to Corelli, ye ken." 5

There was something odd in this speech, and the tone in which it was said. It seemed as if my companion was not always in his constant mind, or that he was willing to try if he could frighten me. I laughed at the extravagance of his language, however, and asked him in 10 reply if he was fool enough to believe that the foul fiend would play so silly a masquerade.

"Ye ken little about it—little about it," said the old man, shaking his head and beard, and knitting his brows. "I could tell ye something about that." 15

What his wife mentioned of his being a tale-teller as well as a musician now occurred to me; and as, you know, I like tales of superstition, I begged to have a specimen of his talent as we went along.

"It is very true," said the blind man, "that when I 20 am tired of scraping thairm or singing ballants I whiles make a tale serve the turn among the country bodies; and

* SIR WALTER SCOTT (1771-1832), poet and novelist, included this story in *Redgauntlet* (1824), a novel belonging to that Waverley series which gave this writer his most enduring rights to fame. See also pp. 26-30.

I have some fearsome anes, that make the auld carlines shake on the settle, and the bits o' bairns skirl on their minnies out frae their beds. But this that I am going to tell you was a thing that befell in our ain house in my
5 father's time—that is, my father was then a hafflins callant; and I tell it to you, that it may be a lesson to you that are but a young thoughtless chap, wha ye draw up wi' on a lonely road; for muckle was the dool and care that came o' 't to my gudesire."

10 He commenced his tale accordingly, in a distinct narrative tone of voice, which he raised and depressed with considerable skill; at times sinking almost into a whisper, and turning his clear but sightless eyeballs upon my face, as if it had been possible for him to witness the im-
15 pression which his narrative made upon my features. I will not spare a syllable of it, although it be of the longest; so I make a dash—and begin:

Ye maun have heard of Sir Robert Redgauntlet of that ilk, who lived in these parts before the dear years. The
20 country will lang mind him; and our fathers used to draw breath thick if ever they heard him named. He was out wi' the Hielandmen in Montrose's time; and again he was in the hills wi' Glencairn in the saxteen hundred and fifty-twa; and sae when King Charles the Second came in,
25 wha was in sic favor as the laird of Redgauntlet? He was knighted at Lonon Court, wi' the king's ain sword; and being a red-hot prelatist, he came down here, rampauging like a lion, with commissions of lieutenancy (and of lunacy, for what I ken), to put down a' the Whigs
30 and Covenanters in the country. Wild wark they made of it; for the Whigs were as dour as the Cavaliers were fierce, and it was which should first tire the other. Redgauntlet was aye for the strong hand; and his name is

kend as wide in the country as Claverhouse's or Tam Dalyell's. Glen, nor dargle, nor mountain, nor cave could hide the puir hill-folk when Redgauntlet was out with bugle and bloodhound after them, as if they had been sae mony deer. And, troth, when they fand them, 5 they didna make muckle mair ceremony than a Hielandman wi' a roebuck. It was just, "Will ye tak' the test?" If not—"Make ready—present—fire!" and there lay the recusant.

Far and wide was Sir Robert hated and feared. Men 10 thought he had a direct compact with Satan; that he was proof against steel and that bullets happed aff his buff-coat like hailstanes from a hearth; that he had a mear that would turn a hare on the side of Carrifra-gauns;* and muckle to the same purpose, of whilk mair anon. The 15 best blessing they wared on him was, "Deil scowp wi' Redgauntlet!" He wasna a bad master to his ain folk, though, and was weel aneugh liked by his tenants; and as for the lackeys and troopers that rade out wi' him to the persecutions, as the Whigs caa'd those killing-times, they 20 wad hae drunken themsells blind to his health at ony time.

Now you are to ken that my gudesire lived on Redgauntlet's grund—they ca' the place Primrose Knowe. We had lived on the grund, and under the Redgauntlets, since the riding-days, and lang before. It was a pleasant 25 bit; and I think the air is callerer and fresher there than onywhere else in the country. It 's a' deserted now; and I sat on the broken door-cheek three days since, and was glad I couldna see the plight the place was in—but that 's a' wide o' the mark. There dwelt my gudesire, 30 Steenie Steenson; a rambling, rattling chiel' he had been in his young days, and could play weel on the pipes; he was famous at "hoopers and girders," a' Cumberland

*** A precipitous side of a mountain in Moffatdale.**

couldna touch him at "Jockie Lattin," and he had the finest finger for the back-lilt between Berwick and Carlisle. The like o' Steenie wasna the sort that they made Whigs o'. And so he became a Tory, as they ca' it, 5 which we now ca' Jacobites, just out of a kind of needcessity, that he might belang to some side or other. He had nae ill-will to the Whig bodies, and liked little to see the blude rin, though, being obliged to follow Sir Robert in hunting and hoisting, watching and warding, he saw 10 muckle mischief, and maybe did some that he couldna avoid.

Now Steenie was a kind of favorite with his master, and kend a' the folk about the castle, and was often sent for to play the pipes when they were at their merriment. 15 Auld Dougal MacCallum, the butler, that had followed Sir Robert through gude and ill, thick and thin, pool and stream, was specially fond of the pipes, and aye gae my gudesire his gude wurd wi' the laird; for Dougal could turn his master round his finger.

20 Weel, round came the Revolution, and it had like to hae broken the hearts baith of Dougal and his master. But the change was not a'thegether sae great as they feared and other folk thought for. The Whigs made an unco crawing what they wad do with their auld enemies, 25 and in special wi' Sir Robert Redgauntlet. But there were owermony great folks dipped in the same doings to make a spick-and-span new warld. So Parliament passed it a' ower easy; and Sir Robert, bating that he was held to hunting foxes instead of Covenanters, remained just 30 the man he was.* His revel was as loud, and his hall

* The caution and moderation of King William III., and his principles of unlimited toleration, deprived the Cameronians of the opportunity they ardently desired, to retaliate the injuries which they had received during the reign of prelacy,

as weel lighted, as ever it had been, though maybe he lacked the fines of the nonconformists, that used to come to stock his larder and cellar; for it is certain he began to be keener about the rents than his tenants used to find him before, and they behooved to be prompt to the rent- 5 day, or else the laird wasna pleased. And he was sic an awsome body that naebody cared to anger him; for the oaths he swore, and the rage that he used to get into, and the looks that he put on made men sometimes think him a devil incarnate. 10

Weel, my gudesire was nae manager—no that he was a very great misguider—but he hadna the saving gift, and he got twa terms' rent in arrear. He got the first brash at Whitsunday put ower wi' fair word and piping; but when Martinmas came there was a summons from the 15 grund officer to come wi' the rent on a day preceese, or else Steenie behooved to flit. Sair wark he had to get the siller; but he was weel freended, and at last he got the haill scraped thegether—a thousand merks. The maist of it was from a neighbor they caa'd Laurie Lapraik—a sly 20 tod. Laurie had wealth o' gear, could hunt wi' the hound and rin wi' the hare, and be Whig or Tory, saunt or sinner, as the wind stood. He was a professor in this Revolution warld, but he liked an orra sough of this warld, and a tune on the pipes, weel aneugh at a by- 25 time; and, bune a', he thought he had gude security for the siller he len my gudesire ower the stocking at Primrose Knowe.

Away trots my gudesire to Redgauntlet Castle wi' a

and purify the land, as they called it, from the pollution of 30 blood. They esteemed the Revolution, therefore, only a half-measure, which neither comprehended the rebuilding the kirk in its full splendor, nor the revenge of the death of the saints on their persecutors.

heavy purse and a light heart, glad to be out of the laird's danger. Weel, the first thing he learned at the castle was that Sir Robert had fretted himsell into a fit of the gout because he did no appear before twelve o'clock.
5 It wasna a'thegether for sake of the money, Dougal thought, but because he didna like to part wi' my gudesire aff the grund. Dougal was glad to see Steenie, and brought him into the great oak parlor; and there sat the laird his leesome lane, excepting that he had beside him
10 a great, ill-favored jackanape that was a special pet of his. A cankered beast it was, and mony an ill-natured trick it played; ill to please it was, and easily angered—ran about the haill castle, chattering and rowling, and pinching and biting folk, specially before ill weather, or dis-
15 turbance in the state. Sir Robert caa'd it Major Weir, after the warlock that was burnt;* and few folk liked either the name or the conditions of the creature—they thought there was something in it by ordinar—and my gudesire was not just easy in mind when the door shut on
20 him, and he saw himsell in the room wi' naebody but the laird, Dougal MacCallum, and the major—a thing that hadna chanced to him before.

Sir Robert sat, or, I should say, lay, in a great armchair, wi' his grand velvet gown, and his feet on a cradle;
25 for he had baith gout and gravel, and his face looked as gash and ghastly as Satan's. Major Weir sat opposite to him, in a red-laced coat, and the laird's wig on his head; and aye as Sir Robert girned wi' pain, the jackanape girned too, like a sheep's head between a pair
30 of tangs—an ill-faur'd, fearsome couple they were. The laird's buff-coat was hung on a pin behind him, and his broadsword and his pistols within reach; for he keepit up

* A celebrated wizard, executed at Edinburgh for sorcery and other crimes.

the auld fashion of having the weapons ready, and a horse saddled day and night, just as he used to do when he was able to loup on horseback, and sway after ony of the hill-folk he could get speerings of. Some said it was for fear of the Whigs taking vengeance, but I judge it 5 was just his auld custom—he wasna gine not fear onything. The rental-book, wi' its black cover and brass clasps, was lying beside him; and a book of sculduddery sangs was put betwixt the leaves, to keep it open at the place where it bore evidence against the goodman of 10 Primrose Knowe, as behind the hand with his mails and duties. Sir Robert gave my gudesire a look, as if he would have withered his heart in his bosom. Ye maun ken he had a way of bending his brows that men saw the visible mark of a horseshoe in his forehead, deep-tinted, as if it 15 had been stamped there.

"Are ye come light-handed, ye son of a toom whistle?" said Sir Robert. "Zounds! if you are——"

My gudesire, with as gude a countenance as he could put on, made a leg, and placed the bag of money on the 20 table wi' a dash, like a man that does something clever. The laird drew it to him hastily. "Is it all here, Steenie, man?"

"Your honor will find it right," said my gudesire.

"Here, Dougal," said the laird, "gie Steenie a tass of 25 brandy, till I count the siller and write the receipt."

But they werena weel out of the room when Sir Robert gied a yelloch that garr'd the castle rock. Back ran Dougal; in flew the liverymen; yell on yell gied the laird, ilk ane mair awfu' than the ither. My gudesire knew not 30 whether to stand or flee, but he ventured back into the parlor, where a' was gaun hirdie-girdie—naebody to say "come in" or "gae out." Terribly the laird roared for cauld water to his feet, and wine to cool his throat;

and "Hell, hell, hell, and its flames," was aye the word in his mouth. They brought him water, and when they plunged his swoln feet into the tub, he cried out it was burning; and folks say that it *did* bubble and sparkle
5 like a seething cauldron. He flung the cup at Dougal's head and said he had given him blood instead of Burgundy; and, sure aneugh, the lass washed clotted blood aff the carpet the neist day. The jackanape they caa'd Major Weir, it jibbered and cried as if it was mocking its mas-
10 ter. My gudesire's head was like to turn; he forgot baith siller and receipt, and downstairs he banged; but, as he ran, the shrieks came fainter and fainter; there was a deep-drawn shivering groan, and word gaed through the castle that the laird was dead.

15 Weel, away came my gudesire wi' his finger in his mouth, and his best hope was that Dougal had seen the money-bag and heard the laird speak of writing the receipt. The young laird, now Sir John, came from Edinburgh to see things put to rights. Sir John and his father
20 never 'greed weel. Sir John had been bred an advocate, and afterward sat in the last Scots Parliament and voted for the Union, having gotten, it was thought, a rug of the compensations—if his father could have come out of his grave he would have brained him for it on his awn
25 hearthstane. Some thought it was easier counting with the auld rough knight than the fair-spoken young ane—but mair of that anon.

Dougal MacCallum, poor body, neither grat nor graned, but gaed about the house looking like a corpse,
30 but directing, as was his duty, a' the order of the grand funeral. Now Dougal looked aye waur and waur when night was coming, and was aye the last to gang to his bed, whilk was in a little round just opposite the chamber of dais, whilk his master occupied while he was living,

and where he now lay in state, as they caa'd it, weeladay! The night before the funeral Dougal could keep his awn counsel nae longer; he came doun wi' his proud spirit, and fairly asked auld Hutcheon to sit in his room with him for an hour. When they were in the round, Dougal took 5 a tass of brandy to himsell, and gave another to Hutcheon, and wished him all health and lang life, and said that, for himsell, he wasna lang for this world; for that every night since Sir Robert's death his silver call had sounded from the state chamber just as it used to do at nights in 10 his lifetime to call Dougal to help to turn him in his bed. Dougal said that, being alone with the dead on that floor of the tower (for naebody cared to wake Sir Robert Redgauntlet like another corpse), he had never daured to answer the call, but that now his conscience checked 15 him for neglecting his duty; for, "though death breaks service," said MacCallum, "it shall never weak my service to Sir Robert; and I will answer his next whistle, so be you will stand by me, Hutcheon."

Hutcheon had nae will to the wark, but he had stood 20 by Dougal in battle and broil, and he wad not fail him at this pinch; so doun the carles sat ower a stoup of brandy, and Hutcheon, who was something of a clerk, would have read a chapter of the Bible; but Dougal would hear naething but a blaud of Davie Lindsay, whilk was the 25 waur preparation.

When midnight came, and the house was quiet as the grave, sure enough the silver whistle sounded as sharp and shrill as if Sir Robert was blowing it; and up got the twa auld serving-men, and tottered into the room where 30 the dead man lay. Hutcheon saw aneugh at the first glance; for there were torches in the room, which showed him the foul fiend, in his ain shape, sitting on the laird's coffin! Ower he couped as if he had been dead. He could not tell how lang he lay in a trance at the door, but when he gathered himsell he cried on his neighbor, and getting nae answer raised the house, when Dougal was found lying dead within twa steps of the bed where 5 his master's coffin was placed. As for the whistle, it was gane anes and aye; but mony a time was it heard at the top of the house on the bartizan, and amang the auld chimneys and turrets where the howlets have their nests. Sir John hushed the matter up, and the funeral passed 10 over without mair bogie wark.

But when a' was ower, and the laird was beginning to settle his affairs, every tenant was called up for his arrears, and my gudesire for the full sum that stood against him in the rental-book. Weel, away he trots to the castle 15 to tell his story, and there he is introduced to Sir John, sitting in his father's chair, in deep mourning, with weepers and hanging cravat, and a small walking-rapier by his side, instead of the auld broadsword that had a hundredweight of steel about it, what with blade, chape, and 20 basket-hilt. I have heard their communings so often tauld ower that I almost think I was there mysell, though I couldna be born at the time. [In fact, Alan, my companion, mimicked, with a good deal of humor, the flattering, conciliating tone of the tenant's address and the 25 hypocritical melancholy of the laird's reply. His grandfather, he said, had, while he spoke, his eye fixed on the rental-book, as if it were a mastiff-dog that he was afraid would spring up and bite him.]

"I wuss ye joy, sir, of the head seat and the white 30 loaf and the brid lairdship. Your father was a kind man to freends and followers; muckle grace to you, Sir John, to fill his shoon—his boots, I suld say, for he seldom wore shoon, unless it were muils when he had the gout."

"Ay, Steenie," quoth the laird, sighing deeply, and

putting his napkin to his een, "his was a sudden call, and he will be missed in the country; no time to set his house in order—weel prepared Godward, no doubt, which is the root of the matter; but he left us behind a tangled hesp to wind, Steenie. Hem! hem! We maun go to 5 business, Steenie; much to do, and little time to do it in."

Here he opened the fatal volume. I have heard of a thing they call Doomsday-book—I am clear it has been a rental of back-ganging tenants. 10

"Stephen," said Sir John, still in the same soft, sleekit tone of voice—"Stephen Stevenson, or Steenson, ye are down here for a year's rent behind the hand—due at last term."

Stephen. Please your honor, Sir John, I paid it to your 15 father.

Sir John. Ye took a receipt, then, doubtless, Stephen, and can produce it?

Stephen. Indeed, I hadna time, an it like your honor; for nae sooner had I set doun the siller, and just as his 20 honor, Sir Robert, that 's gaen, drew it till him to count it and write out the receipt, he was ta'en wi' the pains that removed him.

"That was unlucky," said Sir John, after a pause. "But ye maybe paid it in the presence of somebody. I 25 want but a *talis qualis* evidence, Stephen. I would go ower-strictly to work with no poor man."

Stephen. Troth, Sir John, there was naebody in the room but Dougal MacCallum, the butler. But, as your honor kens, he has e'en followed his auld master. 30

"Very unlucky again, Stephen," said Sir John, without altering his voice a single note. "The man to whom ye paid the money is dead, and the man who witnessed the payment is dead too; and the siller which should have been to the fore, is neither seen nor heard tell of in the repositories. How am I to believe a' this?"

Stephen. I dinna ken, your honor; but there is a bit memorandum note of the very coins, for, God help me!
5 I had to borrow out of twenty purses; and I am sure that ilka man there set down will take his grit oath for what purpose I borrowed the money.

Sir John. I have little doubt ye *borrowed* the money, Steenie. It is the *payment* that I want to have proof of.

10 *Stephen.* The siller maun be about the house, Sir John. And since your honor never got it, and his honor that was canna have ta'en it wi' him, maybe some of the family may hae seen it.

Sir John. We will examine the servants, Stephen; that
15 is but reasonable.

But lackey and lass, and page and groom, all denied stoutly that they had even seen such a bag of money as my gudesire described. What was waur, he had unluckily not mentioned to any living soul of them his purpose of
20 paying his rent. Ae quean had noticed something under his arm, but she took it for the pipes.

Sir John Redgauntlet ordered the servants out of the room and then said to my gudesire: "Now, Steenie, ye see ye have fair play; and, as I have little doubt ye ken
25 better where to find the siller than ony other body, I beg in fair terms, and for your own sake, that you will end this fasherie; for, Stephen, ye maun pay or flit."

"The Lord forgie your opinion," said Stephen, driven almost to his wit's end—"I am an honest man."

30 "So am I, Stephen," said his honor; "and so are all the folks in this house, I hope. But if there be a knave among us, it must be he that tells the story he cannot prove." He paused, and then added, mair sternly: "If I understand your trick, sir, you want to take advantage

of some malicious reports concerning things in this family, and particularly respecting my father's sudden death, thereby to cheat me out of the money, and perhaps take away my character by insinuating that I have received the rent I am demanding. Where do you suppose this money to be? I insist upon knowing."

My gudesire saw everything look so muckle against him that he grew nearly desperate. However, he shifted from one foot to another, looked to every corner of the room, and made no answer.

"Speak out, sirrah," said the laird, assuming a look of his father's, a very particular ane, which he had when he was angry—it seemed as if the wrinkles of his frown made that selfsame fearful shape of a horse's shoe in the middle of his brow; "speak out, sir! I *will* know your thoughts; do you suppose that I have this money?"

"Far be it frae me to say so," said Stephen.

"Do you charge any of my people with having taken it?"

"I wad be laith to charge them that may be innocent," said my gudesire; "and if there be any one that is guilty, I have nae proof."

"Somewhere the money must be, if there is a word of truth in your story," said Sir John; "I ask where you think it is—and demand a correct answer!"

"In hell, if you *will* have my thoughts of it," said my gudesire, driven to extremity—"in hell! with your father, his jackanape, and his silver whistle."

Down the stairs he ran (for the parlor was nae place for him after such a word) and he heard the laird swearing blood and wounds behind him, as fast as ever did Sir Robert, and roaring for the bailie and the baron-officer.

Away rode my gudesire to his chief creditor (him they caa'd Laurie Lapraik), to try if he could make onything out of him; but when he tauld his story, he got but the worst word in his wame—thief, beggar, and dyvour were the saftest terms; and to the boot of these hard terms, Laurie brought up the auld story of dipping his 5 hand in the blood of God's saunts, just as if a tenant could have helped riding with the laird, and that a laird like Sir Robert Redgauntlet. My gudesire was, by this time, far beyond the bounds of patience, and, while he and Laurie were at deil speed the liars, he was wanchancie 10 aneugh to abuse Lapraik's doctrine as weel as the man, and said things that garr'd folks' flesh grue that heard them—he wasna just himsell, and he had lived wi' a wild set in his day.

At last they parted, and my gudesire was to ride hame 15 through the wood of Pitmurkie, that is a' fou of black firs, as they say. I ken the wood, but the firs may be black or white for what I can tell. At the entry of the wood there is a wild common, and on the edge of the common a little lonely change-house, that was keepit then by an 20 hostler wife—they suld hae caa'd her Tibbie Faw—and there puir Steenie cried for a mutchkin of brandy, for he had had no refreshment the haill day. Tibbie was earnest wi' him to take a bite of meat, but he couldna think o' 't, nor would he take his foot out of the stirrup, and took 25 off the brandy wholely at twa draughts, and named a toast at each. The first was, the memory of Sir Robert Redgauntlet, and may he never lie quiet in his grave till he had righted his poor bond-tenant; and the second was, a health to Man's Enemy, if he would but get him 30 back the pock of siller, or tell him what came o' 't, for he saw the haill world was like to regard him as a thief and a cheat, and he took that waur than even the ruin of his house and hauld.

On he rode, little caring where. It was a dark night

turned, and the trees made it yet darker, and he let the beast take its ain road through the wood; when all of a sudden, from tired and wearied that it was before, the nag began to spring and flee and stend, that my gudesire could hardly keep the saddle. Upon the whilk, a horse- 5 man, suddenly riding up beside him, said: "That 's a mettle beast of yours, freend; will you sell him?" So saying, he touched the horse's neck with his riding-wand, and it fell into its auld heigh-ho of a stumbling trot. "But his spunk 's soon out of him, I think," continued 10 the stranger, "and that is like mony a man's courage, that thinks he wad do great things."

My gudesire scarce listened to this, but spurred his horse, with: "Gude-e'en to you, freend."

But it 's like the stranger was ane that doesna lightly 15 yield his point; for, ride as Steenie liked, he was aye beside him at the selfsame pace. At last my gudesire, Steenie Steenson, grew half angry, and, to say the truth, half feard.

"What is it that you want with me, freend?" he 20 said. "If ye be a robber, I have nae money; if ye be a leal man, wanting company, I have nae heart to mirth or speaking; and if ye want to ken the road, I scarce ken it mysell."

"If you will tell me your grief," said the stranger, 25 "I am one that, though I have been sair miscaa'd in the world, am the only hand for helping my freends."

So my gudesire, to ease his ain heart, mair than from any hope of help, told him the story from beginning to end. 30

"It's a hard pinch," said the stranger; "but I think I can help you."

"If you could lend the money, sir, and take a lang day—I ken nae other help on earth," said my gudesire.

"But there may be some under the earth," said the stranger. "Come, I'll be frank wi' you; I could lend you the money on bond, but you would maybe scruple my terms. Now I can tell you that your auld laird is dis-
5 turbed in his grave by your curses and the wailing of your family, and if ye daur venture to go to see him, he will give you the receipt."

My gudesire's hair stood on end at this proposal, but he thought his companion might be some humorsome
10 chield that was trying to frighten him, and might end with lending him the money. Besides he was bauld wi' brandy, and desperate wi' distress; and he said he had courage to go to the gate of hell, and a step farther, for that receipt. The stranger laughed.

15 Weel, they rode on through the thickest of the wood, when, all of a sudden, the horse stopped at the door of a great house; and, but that he knew the place was ten miles off, my father would have thought he was at Red-gauntlet Castle. They rode into the outer courtyard,
20 through the muckle faulding yetts, and aneath the auld portcullis; and the whole front of the house was lighted, and there were pipes and fiddles, and as much dancing and deray within as used to be at Sir Robert's house at Pace and Yule, and such high seasons. They lap off, and
25 my gudesire, as seemed to him, fastened his horse to the very ring he had tied him to that morning when he gaed to wait on the young Sir John.

"God!" said my gudesire, "if Sir Robert's death be but a dream!"

30 He knocked at the ha' door just as he was wont, and his auld acquaintance, Dougal MacCallum—just after his wont, too—came to open the door, and said: "Piper Steenie, are ye there, lad? Sir Robert has been crying for you."

My gudesire was like a man in a dream—he looked for the stranger, but he was gane for the time. At last he just tried to say: "Ha! Dougal Driveower, are you living? I thought ye had been dead."

"Never fash yoursell wi' me," said Dougal, "but look to yoursell; and see ye tak' naething frae onybody here, neither meat, drink, or siller, except the receipt that is your ain."

So saying, he led the way out through halls and trances that were weel kend to my gudesire, and into the auld oak parlor; and there was as much singing of profane sangs, and birling of red wine, and blasphemy and sculduddery as had ever been in Redgauntlet Castle when it was at the blythest.

But Lord take us in keeping! what a set of ghastly revelers there were that sat around that table! My gudesire kend mony that had long before gane to their place, for often had he piped to the most part in the hall of Redgauntlet. There was the fierce Middleton, and the dissolute Rothes, and the crafty Lauderdale; and Dalyell, with his bald head and a beard to his girdle; and Earlshall, with Cameron's blude on his hand; and wild Bonshaw, that tied blessed Mr. Cargill's limbs till the blude sprung; and Dumbarton Douglas, the twice-turned traitor baith to country and king. There was the Bludy Advocate MacKenyie, who, for his worldly wit and wisdom, had been to the rest as a god. And there was Claverhouse, as beautiful as when he lived, with his long, dark, curled locks streaming down over his laced buff-coat, and with his left hand always on his right spule-blade, to hide the wound that the silver bullet had made.* He sat apart from them all, and looked at them

* The personages here mentioned are most of them characters of historical fame; but those less known and remem-

with a melancholy, haughty countenance; while the rest hallooed and sang and laughed, that the room rang. But their smiles were fearfully contorted from time to time; and their laughter passed into such wild sounds as 5 made my gudesire's very nails grow blue, and chilled the marrow in his banes.

They that waited at the table were just the wicked serving-men and troopers that had done their work and cruel bidding on earth. There was the Lang Lad of the 10 Nethertown, that helped to take Argyle; and the bishop's summoner, that they called the Deil's Rattlebag; and the wicked guardsmen in their laced coats; and the savage Highland Amorites, that shed blood like water; and mony a proud serving-man, haughty of heart and bloody 15 of hand, cringing to the rich, and making them wickeder than they would be; grinding the poor to powder when the rich had broken them to fragments. And mony, mony mair were coming and ganging, a' as busy in their vocation as if they had been alive.

20 Sir Robert Redgauntlet, in the midst of a' this fearful riot, cried, wi' a voice like thunder, on Steenie Piper to come to the board-head where he was sitting, his legs stretched out before him, and swathed up with flannel, with his holster pistols aside him, while the great broad-25 sword rested against his chair, just as my gudesire had seen him the last time upon earth; the very cushion for the jackanape was close to him; but the creature itsell was not there—it wasna its hour, it 's likely; for he heard them say, as he came forward: "Is not the major come

30 bered may be found in the tract entitled The Judgment and Justice of God Exemplified; or, A Brief Historical Account of some of the Wicked Lives and Miserable Deaths of some of the most Remarkable Apostates and Bloody Persecutors, from the Reformation till after the Revolution.

yet?" And another answered: "The jackanape will be here betimes the morn." And when my gudesire came forward, Sir Robert, or his ghaist, or the deevil in his likeness, said: "Weel, piper, hae ye settled wi' my son for the year's rent?" 5

With much ado my father gat breath to say that Sir John would not settle without his honor's receipt.

"Ye shall hae that for a tune of the pipes, Steenie," said the appearance of Sir Robert—"play us up Weel Hoddled, Luckie." 10

Now this was a tune my gudesire learned frae a warlock, that heard it when they were worshiping Satan at their meetings; and my gudesire had sometimes played it at the ranting suppers in Redgauntlet Castle, but never very willingly; and now he grew cauld at the very 15 name of it, and said, for excuse, he hadna his pipes wi' him.

"MacCallum, ye limb of Beelzebub," said the fearfu' Sir Robert, "bring Steenie the pipes that I am keeping for him!" 20

MacCallum brought a pair of pipes might have served the piper of Donald of the Isles. But he gave my gudesire a nudge as he offered them; and looking secretly and closely, Steenie saw that the chanter was of steel, and heated to a white heat; so he had fair warning not to 25 trust his fingers with it. So he excused himsell again, and said he was faint and frightened, and had not wind aneugh to fill the bag.

"Then ye maun eat and drink, Steenie," said the figure; "for we do little else here; and it 's ill speak- 30 ing between a fou man and a fasting." Now these were the very words that the bloody Earl of Douglas said to keep the king's messenger in hand while he cut the head off MacLellan of Bombie, at the Threave Castle; * and that put Steenie mair and mair on his guard. So he spoke up like a man, and said he came neither to eat nor drink, nor make minstrelsy; but simply for his ain—to ken what was come o' the money he had paid, and to get a discharge for it; and he was so stout-hearted by this time that he charged Sir Robert for conscience's sake (he had no power to say the holy name), and as he hoped for peace and rest, to spread no snares for him, but just to give him his ain.

The appearance gnashed its teeth and laughed, but it took from a large pocket-book the receipt, and handed it to Steenie. "There is your receipt, ye pitiful cur; and for the money, my dog-whelp of a son may go look for it in the Cat's Cradle."

My gudesire uttered mony thanks, and was about to retire, when Sir Robert roared aloud: "Stop, though, thou sack-doudling son of a —! I am not done with thee. HERE we do nothing for nothing; and you must return on this very day twelvemonth to pay your master the homage that you owe me for my protection."

My father's tongue was loosed of a suddenty, and he said aloud: "I refer myself to God's pleasure, and not to yours."

He had no sooner uttered the word than all was dark around him; and he sank on the earth with such a sudden shock that he lost both breath and sense.

How lang Steenie lay there he could not tell; but when he came to himself he was lying in the auld kirkyard of Redgauntlet parochine, just at the door of the family aisle, and the scutcheon of the auld knight, Sir Robert, hanging over his head. There was a deep morn-

* The reader is referred for particulars to Pitscottie's History of Scotland.

ing fog on grass and gravestane around him, and his horse was feeding quietly beside the minister's twa cows. Steenie would have thought the whole was a dream, but he had the receipt in his hand fairly written and signed by the auld laird; only the last letters of his name were 5 a little disorderly, written like one seized with sudden pain.

Sorely troubled in his mind, he left that dreary place, rode through the mist to Redgauntlet Castle, and with much ado he got speech of the laird. 10

"Well, you dyvour bankrupt," was the first word, "have you brought me my rent?"

"No," answered my gudesire, "I have not; but I have brought your honor Sir Robert's receipt for it."

"How, sirrah? Sir Robert's receipt! You told me he 15 had not given you one."

"Will your honor please to see if that bit line is right?"

Sir John looked at every line, and at every letter, with much attention; and at last at the date, which my 20 gudesire had not observed—"From my appointed place," he read, "this twenty-fifth of November."

"What! That is yesterday! Villain, thou must have gone to hell for this!"

"I got it from your honor's father; whether he be in 25 heaven or hell, I know not," said Steenie.

"I will debate you for a warlock to the Privy Council!" said Sir John. "I will send you to your master, the devil, with the help of a tar-barrel and a torch!"

"I intend to debate mysell to the Presbytery," said 30 Steenie, "and tell them all I have seen last night, whilk are things fitter for them to judge of than a borrel man like me."

Sir John paused, composed himsell, and desired to hear

the full history; and my gudesire told it him from point to point, as I have told it you—neither more nor less.

Sir John was silent again for a long time, and at last he said, very composedly: "Steenie, this story of yours
5 concerns the honor of many a noble family besides mine; and if it be a leasing-making, to keep yourself out of my danger, the least you can expect is to have a red-hot iron driven through your tongue, and that will be as bad as scaulding your fingers wi' a red-hot chanter. But yet it
10 may be true, Steenie; and if the money cast up, I shall not know what to think of it. But where shall we find the Cat's Cradle? There are cats enough about the old house, but I think they kitten without the ceremony of bed or cradle."

15 "We were best ask Hutcheon," said my gudesire; "he kens a' the odd corners about as weel as—another serving-man that is now gane, and that I wad not like to name."

Aweel, Hutcheon, when he was asked, told them that
20 a ruinous turret lang disused, next the clock-house, only accessible by a ladder, for the opening was on the outside, above the battlements, was called of old the Cat's Cradle.

"There will I go immediately," said Sir John; and
25 he took—with what purpose Heaven kens—one of his father's pistols from the hall-table, where they had lain since the night he died, and hastened to the battlements.

It was a dangerous place to climb, for the ladder was
30 auld and frail, and wanted ane or twa rounds. However, up got Sir John, and entered at the turret door, where his body stopped the only little light that was in the bit turret. Something flees at him wi' a vengeance, maist dang him back ower—bang! gaed the knight's

pistol, and Hutcheon, that held the ladder, and my gudesire, that stood beside him, hears a loud skelloch. A minute after, Sir John flings the body of the jackanape down to them, and cries that the siller is fund, and that they should come up and help him. And there was the bag of siller sure aneugh, and mony orra thing besides, that had been missing for mony a day. And Sir John, when he had riped the turret weel, led my gudesire into the dining-parlor, and took him by the hand, and spoke kindly to him, and said he was sorry he should have doubted his word, and that he would hereafter be a good master to him, to make amends.

"And now, Steenie," said Sir John, "although this vision of yours tends, on the whole, to my father's credit as an honest man, that he should, even after his death, desire to see justice done to a poor man like you, yet you are sensible that ill-dispositioned men might make bad constructions upon it concerning his soul's health. So, I think, we had better lay the haill dirdum on that ill-deedie creature, Major Weir, and say naething about your dream in the wood of Pitmurkie. You had taen ower-muckle brandy to be very certain about onything; and, Steenie, this receipt"—his hand shook while he held it out—"it 's but a queer kind of document, and we will do best, I think, to put it quietly in the fire."

"Od, but for as queer as it is, it 's a' the voucher I have for my rent," said my gudesire, who was afraid, it may be, of losing the benefit of Sir Robert's discharge.

"I will bear the contents to your credit in the rental-book, and give you a discharge under my own hand," said Sir John, "and that on the spot. And, Steenie, if you can hold your tongue about this matter, you shall sit, from this time downward, at an easier rent."

"Mony thanks to your honor," said Steenie, who saw

easily in what corner the wind was; " doubtless I will be conformable to all your honor's commands; only I would willingly speak wi' some powerful minister on the subject, for I do not like the sort of soumons of appoint-
5 ment whilk your honor's father——"

" Do not call the phantom my father!" said Sir John, interrupting him.

" Weel then, the thing that was so like him," said my gudesire; " he spoke of my coming back to see him
10 this time twelvemonth, and it 's a weight on my conscience."

" Aweel then," said Sir John, " if you be so much distressed in mind, you may speak to our minister of the parish; he is a douce man, regards the honor of our
15 family, and the mair that he may look for some patronage from me."

Wi' that, my father readily agreed that the receipt should be burned; and the laird threw it into the chimney with his ain hand. Burn it would not for them, though;
20 but away it flew up the lum, wi' a lang train of sparks at its tail, and a hissing noise like a squib.

My gudesire gaed down to the manse, and the minister, when he had heard the story, said it was his real opinion that, though my gudesire had gane very far in
25 tampering with dangerous matters, yet as he had refused the devil's arles (for such was the offer of meat and drink), and had refused to do homage by piping at his bidding, he hoped that, if he held a circumspect walk hereafter, Satan could take little advantage by what was
30 come and gane. And, indeed, my gudesire, of his ain accord, lang forswore baith the pipes and the brandy—it was not even till the year was out, and the fatal day past, that he would so much as take the fiddle or drink usquebaugh or tippenny.

Sir John made up his story about the jackanape as he liked himsell; and some believe till this day there was no more in the matter than the filching nature of the brute. Indeed, ye'll no hinder some to threap, that it was nane o' the auld Enemy that Dougal and Hutcheon 5 saw in the laird's room, but only that wanchancie creature the major, capering on the coffin; and that, as to the blawing on the laird's whistle that was heard after he was dead, the filthy brute could do that as weel as the laird himsell, if not better. But Heaven kens the truth, 10 whilk first came out by the minister's wife, after Sir John and her ain gudeman were baith in the moulds. And then my gudesire, wha was failed in his limbs, but not in his judgment or memory—at least nothing to speak of—was obliged to tell the real narrative to his 15 freends, for the credit of his good name. He might else have been charged for a warlock.*

The shades of evening were growing thicker around us as my conductor finished his long narrative with this moral: "You see, birkie, it is nae chancy thing to tak' a 20 stranger traveler for a guide when you are in an uncouth land."

"I should not have made that inference," said I. "Your grandfather's adventure was fortunate for himself, whom it saved from ruin and distress; and fortu- 25 nate for his landlord."

*I have heard in my youth some such wild tale as that placed in the mouth of the blind fiddler, of which, I think, the hero was Sir Robert Grierson, of Lagg, the famous persecutor. But the belief was general throughout Scotland that 30 the excessive lamentation over the loss of friends disturbed the repose of the dead, and broke even the rest of the grave. [Here, and on p. 123, only the essential parts of the author's notes are reprinted.]

"Ay, but they had baith to sup the sauce o' 't sooner or later," said Wandering Willie; "what was fristed wasna forgiven. Sir John died before he was much over threescore; and it was just like of a moment's illness. 5 And for my gudesire, though he departed in fullness of life, yet there was my father, a yauld man of forty-five, fell down betwixt the stilts of his plough, and raise never again, and left nae bairn but me, a puir, sightless, fatherless, motherless creature, could neither work nor want. 10 Things gaed weel aneugh at first; for Sir Regwald Redgauntlet, the only son of Sir John and the oye of auld Sir Robert, and, wae 's me! the last of the honorable house, took the farm aff our hands, and brought me into his household to have care of me. My head never settled 15 since I lost him; and if I say another word about it, deil a bar will I have the heart to play the night. Look out, my gentle chap," he resumed, in a different tone; "ye should see the lights at Brokenburn Glen by this time."

THE MASQUE OF THE RED DEATH *

By EDGAR ALLAN POE

The "Red Death" had long devastated the country. No pestilence had ever been so fatal, or so hideous. Blood was its Avatar and its seal—the redness and the horror of blood. There were sharp pains, and sudden dizziness, and then profuse bleeding at the pores, with 5 dissolution. The scarlet stains upon the body, and especially upon the face of the victim, were the pest ban which shut him out from the aid and from the sympathy of his fellow-men. And the whole seizure, progress, and termination of the disease were the incidents of half an 10 hour.

But the Prince Prospero was happy and dauntless and sagacious. When his dominions were half depopulated, he summoned to his presence a thousand hale and light-hearted friends from among the knights and dames of his 15 court, and with these retired to the deep seclusion of one of his castellated abbeys. This was an extensive and magnificent structure, the creation of the prince's own eccentric yet august taste. A strong and lofty wall girdled it in. This wall had gates of iron. The courtiers, hav- 20 ing entered, brought furnaces and massy hammers and welded the bolts. They resolved to leave means neither

* Edgar Allan Poe (1804-1849), author of this narrative, has been the most eminent American writer of poetry and short stories. This story was first published in 1842. See also pp. 26-39, 43-50, 54, 56.

of ingress nor egress to the sudden impulses of despair or of frenzy from within. The abbey was amply provisioned. With such precautions the courtiers might bid defiance to contagion. The external world could take
5 care of itself. In the meantime it was folly to grieve, or to think. The prince had provided all the appliances of pleasure. There were buffoons, there were improvvisatori, there were ballet-dancers, there were musicians, there was Beauty, there was wine. All these and security
10 were within. Without was the "Red Death."

It was toward the close of the fifth or sixth month of his seclusion, and while the pestilence raged most furiously abroad, that the Prince Prospero entertained his thousand friends at a masked ball of the most unusual
15 magnificence.

It was a voluptuous scene, that masquerade. But first let me tell of the rooms in which it was held. There were seven—an imperial suite. In many palaces, however, such suites form a long and straight vista, while
20 the folding doors slide back nearly to the walls on either hand, so that the view of the whole extent is scarcely impeded. Here the case was very different; as might have been expected from the duke's love of the *bizarre*. The apartments were so irregularly disposed that the
25 vision embraced but little more than one at a time. There was a sharp turn at every twenty or thirty yards, and at each turn a novel effect. To the right and left, in the middle of each wall, a tall and narrow Gothic window looked out upon a closed corridor which pursued the windings of
30 the suite. These windows were of stained glass whose color varied in accordance with the prevailing hue of the decorations of the chamber into which it opened. That at the eastern extremity was hung, for example, in blue—and vividly blue were its windows. The second

chamber was purple in its ornaments and tapestries, and
here the panes were purple. The third was green throughout, and so were the casements. The fourth was fur-
nished and lighted with orange—the fifth with white—the
sixth with violet. The seventh apartment was closely
shrouded in black velvet tapestries that hung all over the
ceiling and down the walls, falling in heavy folds upon
a carpet of the same material and hue. But in this
chamber only, the color of the windows failed to cor-
respond with the decorations. The panes here were
scarlet—a deep blood color. Now, in no one of the
seven apartments was there any lamp or candelabrum,
amid the profusion of golden ornaments that lay scattered to and fro or depended from the roof. There was
no light of any kind emanating from lamp or candle
within the suite of chambers. But in the corridors that
followed the suite, there stood, opposite to each window, a heavy tripod, bearing a brazier of fire, that projected its rays through the tinted glass and so glaringly
illumined the room. And thus were produced a multitude of gaudy and fantastic appearances. But in the
western or black chamber the effect of the firelight that
streamed upon the dark hangings through the blood-tinted
panes was ghastly in the extreme, and produced so wild
a look upon the countenances of those who entered, that
there were few of the company bold enough to set foot
within its precincts at all.

It was in this apartment, also, that there stood against
the western wall, a gigantic clock of ebony. Its pen-
dulum swung to and fro with a dull, heavy, monotonous
clang; and when the minute-hand made the circuit of the
face, and the hour was to be stricken, there came from
the brazen lungs of the clock a sound which was clear
and loud and deep and exceedingly musical, but of so

peculiar a note and emphasis that, at each lapse of an hour, the musicians of the orchestra were constrained to pause, momentarily, in their performance, to hearken to the sound; and thus the waltzers perforce ceased their evolu-
5 tions; and there was a brief disconcert of the whole gay company; and, while the chimes of the clock yet rang, it was observed that the giddiest grew pale, and the more aged and sedate passed their hands over their brows as if in confused revery or meditation. But when the echoes
10 had fully ceased, a light laughter at once pervaded the assembly; the musicians looked at each other and smiled as if at their own nervousness and folly, and made whispering vows, each to the other, that the next chiming of the clock should produce in them no similar emo-
15 tion; and then, after the lapse of sixty minutes (which embraced three thousand and six hundred seconds of the Time that flies), there came yet another chiming of the clock, and then were the same disconcert and tremulousness and meditation as before.

20 But, in spite of these things, it was a gay and magnificent revel. The tastes of the duke were peculiar. He had a fine eye for colors and effects. He disregarded the *decora* of mere fashion. His plans were bold and fiery, and his conceptions glowed with barbaric luster.
25 There are some who would have thought him mad. His followers felt that he was not. It was necessary to hear and see and touch him to be *sure* that he was not.

He had directed, in great part, the movable embellishments of the seven chambers, upon occasion of this great
30 *fête;* and it was his own guiding taste which had given the character to the masqueraders. Be sure they were grotesque. There were much glare and glitter and piquancy and phantasm—much of what has been since seen in "Hernani." There were arabesque figures with unsuited

limbs and appointments. There were delirious fancies such as the madman fashions. There were much of the beautiful, much of the wanton, much of the *bizarre,* something of the terrible, and not a little of that which might have excited disgust. To and fro in the seven chambers there stalked, in fact, a multitude of dreams. And these —the dreams—writhed in and about, taking hue from the rooms, and causing the wild music of the orchestra to seem as the echo of their steps. And, anon, there strikes the ebony clock which stands in the hall of the velvet. And then, for a moment, all is still, and all is silent save the voice of the clock. The dreams are stiff-frozen as they stand. But the echoes of the chime die away—they have endured but an instant—and a light, half-subdued laughter floats after them as they depart. And now again the music swells, and the dreams live, and writhe to and fro more merrily than ever, taking hue from the many-tinted windows through which stream the rays from the tripods. But to the chamber which lies most westwardly of the seven there are now none of the maskers who venture; for the night is waning away; and there flows a ruddier light through the blood-colored panes; and the blackness of the sable drapery appalls; and to him whose foot falls upon the sable carpet, there comes from the near clock of ebony a muffled peal more solemnly emphatic than any which reaches *their* ears who indulge in the more remote gayeties of the other apartments.

But these other apartments were densely crowded, and in them beat feverishly the heart of life. And the revel went whirlingly on, until at length there commenced the sounding of midnight upon the clock. And then the music ceased, as I have told; and the evolutions of the waltzers were quieted; and there was an uneasy cessation of all things as before. But now there were twelve strokes to be sounded by the bell of the clock; and thus it happened, perhaps, that more of thought crept, with more of time, into the meditations of the thoughtful among those who reveled. And thus, too, it happened, perhaps, that before the last echoes of the last chime had utterly sunk into silence, there were many individuals in the crowd who had found leisure to become aware of the presence of a masked figure which had arrested the attention of no single individual before. And the rumor of this new presence having spread itself whisperingly around, there arose at length from the whole company a buzz, or murmur, expressive of disapprobation and surprise—then, finally, of terror, of horror, and of disgust.

In an assembly of phantasms such as I have painted, it may well be supposed that no ordinary appearance could have excited such sensation. In truth the masquerade license of the night was nearly unlimited; but the figure in question had out-Heroded Herod, and gone beyond the bounds of even the prince's indefinite decorum. There are chords in the hearts of the most reckless which cannot be touched without emotion. Even with the utterly lost, to whom life and death are equally jests, there are matters of which no jest can be made. The whole company, indeed, seemed now deeply to feel that in the costume and bearing of the stranger neither wit nor propriety existed. The figure was tall and gaunt, and shrouded from head to foot in the habiliments of the grave. The mask which concealed the visage was made so nearly to resemble the countenance of a stiffened corpse that the closest scrutiny must have had difficulty in detecting the cheat. And yet all this might have been endured, if not approved, by the mad revelers around.

But the mummer had gone so far as to assume the type of the Red Death. His vesture was dabbled in *blood*—and his broad brow, with all the features of the face, was besprinkled with the scarlet horror.

When the eyes of Prince Prospero fell upon this spectral image (which, with a slow and solemn movement, as if more fully to sustain its *rôle,* stalked to and fro among the waltzers) he was seen to be convulsed, in the first moment with a strong shudder either of terror or distaste; but, in the next, his brow reddened with rage.

"Who dares"—he demanded hoarsely of the courtiers who stood near him—"who dares insult us with this blasphemous mockery? Seize him and unmask him—that we may know whom we have to hang, at sunrise, from the battlements!"

It was in the eastern or blue chamber in which stood the Prince Prospero as he uttered these words. They rang throughout the seven rooms loudly and clearly, for the prince was a bold and robust man, and the music had become hushed at the waving of his hand.

It was in the blue room where stood the prince, with a group of pale courtiers by his side. At first, as he spoke, there was a slight rushing movement of this group in the direction of the intruder, who, at the moment, was also near at hand, and now, with deliberate and stately step, made closer approach to the speaker. But from a certain nameless awe with which the mad assumptions of the mummer had inspired the whole party, there were found none who put forth hand to seize him; so that, unimpeded, he passed within a yard of the prince's person; and, while the vast assembly, as if with one impulse, shrank from the centers of the rooms to the walls, he made his way uninterruptedly, but with the same solemn and measured step which had distinguished him from the first, through the blue chamber to the purple—through the purple to the green—through the green to the orange—through this again to the white—and even thence to the violet, ere a decided movement had been made to arrest him. It was then, however, that the Prince Prospero, maddening with rage and the shame of his own momentary cowardice, rushed hurriedly through the six chambers, while none followed him on account of a deadly terror that had seized upon all. He bore aloft a drawn dagger, and had approached, in rapid impetuosity, to within three or four feet of the retreating figure, when the latter, having attained the extremity of the velvet apartment, turned suddenly and confronted his pursuer. There was a sharp cry—and the dagger dropped gleaming upon the sable carpet, upon which, instantly afterward, fell prostrate in death the Prince Prospero. Then, summoning the wild courage of despair, a throng of the revelers at once threw themselves into the black apartment, and, seizing the mummer, whose tall figure stood erect and motionless within the shadow of the ebony clock, gasped in unutterable horror at finding the grave cerements and corpse-like mask, which they handled with so violent a rudeness, untenanted by any tangible form.

And now was acknowledged the presence of the Red Death. He had come like a thief in the night. And one by one dropped the revelers in the blood-bedewed halls of their revel, and died each in the despairing posture of his fall. And the life of the ebony clock went out with that of the last of the gay. And the flames of the tripods expired. And Darkness and Decay and the Red Death held illimitable dominion over all.

THE GOLD-BUG *

By EDGAR ALLAN POE

What ho! what ho! this fellow is dancing mad!
He hath been bitten by the Tarantula.

—All in the Wrong.

Many years ago, I contracted an intimacy with a Mr. William Legrand. He was of an ancient Huguenot 5 family, and had once been wealthy; but a series of misfortunes had reduced him to want. To avoid the mortification consequent upon his disasters, he left New Orleans, the city of his forefathers, and took up his residence at Sullivan's Island, near Charleston, South Carolina. 10

This island is a very singular one. It consists of little else than the sea sand, and is about three miles long. Its breadth at no point exceeds a quarter of a mile. It is separated from the mainland by a scarcely perceptible creek, oozing its way through a wilderness of reeds and 15 slime, a favorite resort of the marsh-hen. The vegetation, as might be supposed, is scant, or at least dwarfish. No trees of any magnitude are to be seen. Near the western extremity, where Fort Moultrie stands, and where are some miserable frame buildings, tenanted dur- 20 ing summer by the fugitives from Charleston dust and fever, may be found, indeed, the bristly palmetto; but the

* See note to *The Masque of the Red Death. The Gold-Bug* was first published in 1843.

whole island, with the exception of this western point, and a line of hard white beach on the seacoast, is covered with a dense undergrowth of the sweet myrtle, so much prized by the horticulturists of England. The shrub 5 here often attains the height of fifteen or twenty feet, and forms an almost impenetrable coppice, burdening the air with its fragrance.

In the utmost recesses of this coppice, not far from the eastern or more remote end of the island, Legrand 10 had built himself a small hut, which he occupied when I first, by mere accident, made his acquaintance. This soon ripened into friendship—for there was much in the recluse to excite interest and esteem. I found him well educated, with unusual powers of mind, but infected with misan- 15 thropy, and subject to perverse moods of alternate enthusiasm and melancholy. He had with him many books, but rarely employed them. His chief amusements were gunning and fishing, or sauntering along the beach and through the myrtles, in quest of shells or entomological 20 specimens;—his collection of the latter might have been envied by a Swammerdamm. In these excursions he was usually accompanied by an old negro, called Jupiter, who had been manumitted before the reverses of the family, but who could be induced, neither by threats nor by 25 promises, to abandon what he considered his right of attendance upon the footsteps of his young "Massa Will." It is not improbable that the relatives of Legrand, conceiving him to be somewhat unsettled in intellect, had contrived to instil this obstinacy into Jupiter, with a view 30 to the supervision and guardianship of the wanderer.

The winters in the latitude of Sullivan's Island are seldom very severe, and in the fall of the year it is a rare event indeed when a fire is considered necessary. About the middle of October, 18—, there occurred, however, a day of remarkable chilliness. Just before sunset I scrambled my way through the evergreens to the hut of my friend, whom I had not visited for several weeks—my residence being at that time in Charleston, a distance of nine miles from the island, while the facilities of 5 passage and re-passage were very far behind those of the present day. Upon reaching the hut I rapped, as was my custom, and, getting no reply, sought for the key where I knew it was secreted, unlocked the door, and went in. A fine fire was blazing upon the hearth. It 10 was a novelty, and by no means an ungrateful one. I threw off an overcoat, took an armchair by the crackling logs, and awaited patiently the arrival of my hosts.

Soon after dark they arrived, and gave me a most 15 cordial welcome. Jupiter, grinning from ear to ear, bustled about to prepare some marsh-hens for supper. Legrand was in one of his fits—how else shall I term them?—of enthusiasm. He had found an unknown bivalve, forming a new genus, and, more than this, he had 20 hunted down and secured, with Jupiter's assistance, a *scarabæus* which he believed to be totally new, but in respect to which he wished to have my opinion on the morrow.

"And why not to-night?" I asked, rubbing my hands 25 over the blaze, and wishing the whole tribe of *scarabæi* at the devil.

"Ah, if I had only known you were here!" said Legrand, "but it's so long since I saw you; and how could I foresee that you would pay me a visit this very 30 night of all others? As I was coming home I met Lieutenant G——, from the fort, and, very foolishly, I lent him the bug; so it will be impossible for you to see it until the morning. Stay here to-night, and I will send

Jup down for it at sunrise. It is the loveliest thing in creation!"

"What?—sunrise?"

"Nonsense! no!—the bug. It is of a brilliant gold color—about the size of a large hickory-nut—with two jet black spots near one extremity of the back, and another, somewhat longer, at the other. The *antennæ* are——"

"Dey aint *no* tin in him, Massa Will, I keep a tellin on you," here interrupted Jupiter; "de bug is a goole-bug, solid, ebery bit of him, inside and all, sep him wing—neber feel half so hebby a bug in my life."

"Well, suppose it is, Jup," replied Legrand, somewhat more earnestly, it seemed to me, than the case demanded, "is that any reason for your letting the birds burn? The color"—here he turned to me—"is really almost enough to warrant Jupiter's idea. You never saw a more brilliant metallic luster than the scales emit—but of this you cannot judge till to-morrow. In the meantime I can give you some idea of the shape." Saying this, he seated himself at a small table, on which were a pen and ink, but no paper. He looked for some in a drawer, but found none.

"Never mind," said he at length, "this will answer;" and he drew from his waistcoat pocket a scrap of what I took to be very dirty foolscap, and made upon it a rough drawing with the pen. While he did this, I retained my seat by the fire, for I was still chilly. When the design was complete, he handed it to me without rising. As I received it, a low growl was heard, succeeded by a scratching at the door. Jupiter opened it, and a large Newfoundland, belonging to Legrand, rushed in, leaped upon my shoulders, and loaded me with caresses; for I had shown him much attention during previous visits.

When his gambols were over, I looked at the paper, and, to speak the truth, found myself not a little puzzled at what my friend had depicted.

"Well!" I said, after contemplating it for some minutes, "this *is* a strange *scarabæus,* I must confess; new 5 to me: never saw anything like it before—unless it was a skull, or a death's-head, which it more nearly resembles than anything else that has come under *my* observation."

"A death's-head!" echoed Legrand—"Oh—yes— 10 well, it has something of that appearance upon paper, no doubt. The two upper black spots look like eyes, eh? and the longer one at the bottom like a mouth—and then the shape of the whole is oval."

"Perhaps so," said I; "but, Legrand, I fear you are 15 no artist. I must wait until I see the beetle itself, if I am to form any idea of its personal appearance."

"Well, I don't know," said he, a little nettled, "I draw tolerably—*should* do it at least—have had good masters, and flatter myself that I am not quite a block- 20 head."

"But, my dear fellow, you are joking then," said I, "this is a very passable *skull,*—indeed, I may say that it is a very *excellent* skull, according to the vulgar notions about such specimens of physiology—and your *scarabæus* 25 must be the queerest *scarabæus* in the world if it resembles it. Why, we may get up a very thrilling bit of superstition upon this hint. I presume you will call the bug *scarabæus caput hominis,* or something of that kind—there are many similar titles in the Natural Histories. 30 But where are the *antennæ* you spoke of?"

"The *antennæ!*" said Legrand, who seemed to be getting unaccountably warm upon the subject; "I am sure you must see the *antennæ.* I made them as distinct as they are in the original insect, and I presume that is sufficient."

"Well, well," I said, "perhaps you have—still I don't see them;" and I handed him the paper without additional remark, not wishing to ruffle his temper; but I was much surprised at the turn affairs had taken; his ill humor puzzled me—and, as for the drawing of the beetle, there were positively *no antennæ* visible, and the whole *did* bear a very close resemblance to the ordinary cuts of a death's-head.

He received the paper very peevishly, and was about to crumple it, apparently to throw it in the fire, when a casual glance at the design seemed suddenly to rivet his attention. In an instant his face grew violently red—in another as excessively pale. For some minutes he continued to scrutinize the drawing minutely where he sat. At length he arose, took a candle from the table, and proceeded to seat himself upon a sea-chest in the farthest corner of the room. Here again he made an anxious examination of the paper; turning it in all directions. He said nothing, however, and his conduct greatly astonished me; yet I thought it prudent not to exacerbate the growing moodiness of his temper by any comment. Presently he took from his coat pocket a wallet, placed the paper carefully in it, and deposited both in a writing-desk, which he locked. He now grew more composed in his demeanor; but his original air of enthusiasm had quite disappeared. Yet he seemed not so much sulky as abstracted. As the evening wore away he became more and more absorbed in revery, from which no sallies of mine could arouse him. It had been my intention to pass the night at the hut, as I had frequently done before, but, seeing my host in this mood, I deemed it proper to take leave. He did not press me to remain, but, as I departed, he shook my hand with even more than his usual cordiality.

It was about a month after this (and during the interval I had seen nothing of Legrand) when I received a visit, at Charleston, from his man, Jupiter. I had never 5 seen the good old negro look so dispirited, and I feared that some serious disaster had befallen my friend.

"Well, Jup," said I, "what is the matter now?—how is your master?"

"Why, to speak de troof, massa, him not so berry well 10 as mought be."

"Not well! I am truly sorry to hear it. What does he complain of?"

"Dar! dat's it!—him nebber plain of notin—but him berry sick for all dat." 15

"*Very* sick, Jupiter!—why didn't you say so at once? Is he confined to bed?"

"No, dat he aint!—he aint find nowhar—dat's just whar de shoe pinch—my mind is got to be berry hebby bout poor Massa Will." 20

"Jupiter, I should like to understand what it is you are talking about. You say your master is sick. Hasn't he told you what ails him?"

"Why, massa, taint worf while for to git mad bout de matter—Massa Will say noffin at all aint de matter 25 wid him—but den what make him go about looking dis here way, wid he head down and he soldiers up, and as white as a gose? And den he keep a syphon all de time——"

"Keeps a what, Jupiter?" 30

"Keeps a syphon wid de figgurs on de slate—de queerest figgurs I ebber did see. Ise gittin to be skeered, I tell you. Hab for to keep mighty tight eye pon him noovers. Todder day he gib me slip fore de sun up and was gone de whole ob de blessed day. I had a big stick ready cut for to gib him d——d good beating when he did come—but Ise sich a fool dat I hadn't de heart arter all—he look so berry poorly."

5 "Eh?—what?—ah yes!—upon the whole I think you had better not be too severe with the poor fellow—don't flog him, Jupiter—he can't very well stand it—but can you form no idea of what has occasioned this illness, or rather this change of conduct? Has anything unpleasant 10 happened since I saw you?"

"No, massa, dey aint bin noffin onpleasant *since* den —'twas *fore* den I'm feared—'twas de berry day you was dare."

"How? what do you mean?"

15 "Why, massa, I mean de bug—dare now."

"The what?"

"De bug—I'm berry sartain dat Massa Will bin bit somewhere bout de head by dat goole-bug."

"And what cause have you, Jupiter, for such a sup-20 position?"

"Claws enuff, massa, and mouff too. I nebber did see sich a d——d bug—he kick and he bite ebery ting what cum near him. Massa Will cotch him fuss, but had for to let him go gin mighty quick, I tell you—den 25 was de time he must ha got de bite. I didn't like de look ob de bug mouff, myself, no how, so I wouldn't take hold ob him wid my finger, but I cotch him wid a piece ob paper dat I found. I rap him up in de paper and stuff piece ob it in he mouff—dat was de way."

30 "And you think, then, that your master was really bitten by the beetle, and that the bite made him sick?"

"I don't tink noffin about it—I nose it. What make him dream bout de goole so much, if taint cause he bit by de goole-bug? Ise heerd bout dem goole-bugs fore dis."

"But how do you know he dreams about gold?"

"How I know? why cause he talk about it in he sleep—dat's how I nose." 5

"Well, Jup, perhaps you are right; but to what fortunate circumstance am I to attribute the honor of a visit from you to-day?"

"What de matter, massa?"

"Did you bring any message from Mr. Legrand?" 10

"No, massa, I bring dis here pissel;" and here Jupiter handed me a note which ran thus:

"MY DEAR ——, Why have I not seen you for so long a time? I hope you have not been so foolish as to take offence at any little *brusquerie* of mine; but no, that 15 is improbable.

"Since I saw you I have had great cause for anxiety. I have something to tell you, yet scarcely know how to tell it, or whether I should tell it at all.

"I have not been quite well for some days past, and 20 poor old Jup annoys me, almost beyond endurance, by his well-meant attentions. Would you believe it?—he had prepared a huge stick, the other day, with which to chastise me for giving him the slip, and spending the day, *solus,* among the hills on the mainland. I verily 25 believe that my ill looks alone saved me a flogging.

"I have made no addition to my cabinet since we met.

"If you can, in any way, make it convenient, come over with Jupiter. *Do* come. I wish to see you *to-night,* upon business of importance. I assure you that it is of 30 the *highest* importance.

"Ever yours,

"WILLIAM LEGRAND."

There was something in the tone of this note which gave me great uneasiness. Its whole style differed materially from that of Legrand. What could he be dreaming of? What new crotchet possessed his excitable brain?
5 What "business of the highest importance" could *he* possibly have to transact? Jupiter's account of him boded no good. I dreaded lest the continued pressure of misfortune had, at length, fairly unsettled the reason of my friend. Without a moment's hesitation, therefore, I pre-
10 pared to accompany the negro.

Upon reaching the wharf, I noticed a scythe and three spades, all apparently new, lying in the bottom of the boat in which we were to embark.

"What is the meaning of all this, Jup?" I inquired.

15 "Him syfe, massa, and spade."

"Very true; but what are they doing here?"

"Him de syfe and de spade what Massa Will sis pon my buying for him in de town, and de debbil's own lot of money I had to gib for em."

20 "But what, in the name of all that is mysterious, is your 'Massa Will' going to do with scythes and spades?"

"Dat's more dan *I* know, and debbil take me if I don't blieve 'tis more dan he know, too. But it's all cum ob de bug."

25 Finding that no satisfaction was to be obtained of Jupiter, whose whole intellect seemed to be absorbed by "de bug," I now stepped into the boat and made sail. With a fair and strong breeze we soon ran into the little cove to the northward of Fort Moultrie, and a walk of
30 some two miles brought us to the hut. It was about three in the afternoon when we arrived. Legrand had been awaiting us in eager expectation. He grasped my hand with a nervous *empressement,* which alarmed me and strengthened the suspicions already entertained. His

countenance was pale, even to ghastliness, and his deep-set eyes glared with unnatural luster. After some inquiries respecting his health, I asked him, not knowing what better to say, if he had yet obtained the *scarabæus* from Lieutenant G——. 5

"Oh, yes," he replied, coloring violently, "I got it from him the next morning. Nothing should tempt me to part with that *scarabæus*. Do you know that Jupiter is quite right about it?"

"In what way?" I asked, with a sad foreboding at 10 heart.

"In supposing it to be a bug of *real gold*." He said this with an air of profound seriousness, and I felt inexpressibly shocked.

"This bug is to make my fortune," he continued, with 15 a triumphant smile, "to reinstate me in my family possessions. Is it any wonder, then, that I prize it? Since Fortune has thought fit to bestow it upon me, I have only to use it properly and I shall arrive at the gold of which it is the index. Jupiter, bring me that 20 *scarabæus!*"

"What! de bug, massa? I'd rudder not go fer trubble dat bug—you mus git him for your own self." Hereupon Legrand arose, with a grave and stately air, and brought me the beetle from a glass case in which it was inclosed. 25 It was a beautiful *scarabæus*, and, at that time, unknown to naturalists—of course a great prize in a scientific point of view. There were two round, black spots near one extremity of the back, and a long one near the other. The scales were exceedingly hard and glossy, with all the ap- 30 pearance of burnished gold. The weight of the insect was very remarkable, and, taking all things into consideration, I could hardly blame Jupiter for his opinion respecting it; but what to make of Legrand's agreement with that opinion, I could not, for the life of me, tell.

"I sent for you," said he, in a grandiloquent tone, when I had completed my examination of the beetle, 5 "I sent for you, that I might have your counsel and assistance in furthering the views of Fate and of the bug——"

"My dear Legrand," I cried, interrupting him, "you are certainly unwell, and had better use some little 10 precautions. You shall go to bed, and I will remain with you a few days, until you get over this. You are feverish and——"

"Feel my pulse," said he.

I felt it, and to say the truth, found not the slightest 15 indication of fever.

"But you may be ill, and yet have no fever. Allow me this once to prescribe for you. In the first place, go to bed. In the next——"

"You are mistaken," he interposed, "I am as well as 20 I can expect to be under the excitement which I suffer. If you really wish me well, you will relieve this excitement."

"And how is this to be done?"

"Very easily. Jupiter and myself are going upon an 25 expedition into the hills, upon the mainland, and, in this expedition, we shall need the aid of some person in whom we can confide. You are the only one we can trust. Whether we succeed or fail, the excitement which you now perceive in me will be equally allayed."

30 "I am anxious to oblige you in any way," I replied; "but do you mean to say that this infernal beetle has any connection with your expedition into the hills?"

"It has."

"Then, Legrand, I can become a party to no such absurd proceeding."

"I am sorry—very sorry—for we shall have to try it by ourselves."

"Try it by yourselves! The man is surely mad!— 5 but stay—how long do you propose to be absent?"

"Probably all night. We shall start immediately, and be back, at all events, by sunrise."

"And will you promise me, upon your honor, that when this freak of yours is over, and the bug business (good 10 God!) settled to your satisfaction, you will then return home and follow my advice implicitly, as that of your physician?"

"Yes; I promise; and now let us be off, for we have no time to lose." 15

With a heavy heart I accompanied my friend. We started about four o'clock—Legrand, Jupiter, the dog, and myself. Jupiter had with him the scythe and spades —the whole of which he insisted upon carrying, more through fear, it seemed to me, of trusting either of 20 the implements within reach of his master, than from any excess of industry or complaisance. His demeanor was dogged in the extreme, and "dat d——d bug" were the sole words which escaped his lips during the journey. For my own part, I had charge of a couple of dark lanterns, 25 while Legrand contented himself with the *scarabæus,* which he carried attached to the end of a bit of whip-cord; twirling it to and fro, with the air of a conjurer, as he went. When I observed this last, plain evidence of my friend's aberration of mind, I could scarcely re- 30 frain from tears. I thought it best, however, to humor his fancy, at least for the present, or until I could adopt some more energetic measures with a chance of success. In the meantime I endeavored, but all in vain, to sound him in regard to the object of the expedition. Having succeeded in inducing me to accompany him, he seemed unwilling to hold conversation upon any topic of minor importance, and to all my questions vouchsafed no other 5 reply than "we shall see!"

We crossed the creek at the head of the island by means of a skiff, and, ascending the high grounds on the shore of the mainland, proceeded in a northwesterly direction, through a tract of country excessively wild and 10 desolate, where no trace of a human footstep was to be seen. Legrand led the way with decision; pausing only for an instant, here and there, to consult what appeared to be certain landmarks of his own contrivance upon a former occasion.

15 In this manner we journeyed for about two hours, and the sun was just setting when we entered a region infinitely more dreary than any yet seen. It was a species of tableland, near the summit of an almost inaccessible hill, densely wooded from base to pinnacle, and inter- 20 spersed with huge crags that appeared to lie loosely upon the soil, and in many cases were prevented from precipitating themselves into the valleys below merely by the support of the trees against which they reclined. Deep ravines, in various directions, gave an air of still sterner 25 solemnity to the scene.

The natural platform to which we had clambered was thickly overgrown with brambles, through which we soon discovered that it would have been impossible to force our way but for the scythe; and Jupiter, by direc- 30 tion of his master, proceeded to clear for us a path to the foot of an enormously tall tulip-tree, which stood, with some eight or ten oaks, upon the level, and far surpassed them all, and all other trees which I had then ever seen, in the beauty of its foliage and form, in the wide spread of its branches, and in the general majesty of its appearance. When we reached this tree, Legrand turned to Jupiter, and asked him if he thought he could climb it. The old man seemed a little staggered by the question, and for some moments made no reply. At 5 length he approached the huge trunk, walked slowly around it, and examined it with minute attention. When he had completed his scrutiny, he merely said:

" Yes, massa, Jup climb any tree he ebber see in he life." 10

" Then up with you as soon as possible, for it will soon be too dark to see what we are about."

" How far mus go up, massa?" inquired Jupiter.

" Get up the main trunk first, and then I will tell you which way to go—and here—stop! take this beetle 15 with you."

" De bug, Massa Will!—de goole-bug!" cried the negro, drawing back in dismay—" what for mus tote de bug way up de tree?—d——n if I do!"

" If you are afraid, Jup, a great big negro like you, 20 to take hold of a harmless little dead beetle, why, you can carry it up by this string—but, if you do not take it up with you in some way, I shall be under the necessity of breaking your head with this shovel."

" What de matter now, massa?" said Jup, evidently 25 shamed into compliance; " always want fur to raise fuss wid old nigger. Was only funnin anyhow. *Me* feered de bug! what I keer for de bug?" Here he took cautiously hold of the extreme end of the string, and, maintaining the insect as far from his person as circumstances would 30 permit, prepared to ascend the tree.

In youth, the tulip-tree, or *Liriodendron Tulipifera,* the most magnificent of American foresters, has a trunk peculiarly smooth, and often rises to a great height without lateral branches; but, in his riper age, the bark becomes gnarled and uneven, while many short limbs make their appearance on the stem. Thus the difficulty of ascension, in the present case, lay more in semblance than 5 in reality. Embracing the huge cylinder, as closely as possible, with his arms and knees, seizing with his hands some projections, and resting his naked toes upon others, Jupiter, after one or two narrow escapes from falling, at length wriggled himself into the first great fork, and 10 seemed to consider the whole business as virtually accomplished. The *risk* of the achievement was, in fact, now over, although the climber was some sixty or seventy feet from the ground.

"Which way mus go now, Massa Will?" he asked.

15 "Keep up the largest branch,—the one on this side," said Legrand. The negro obeyed him promptly, and apparently with but little trouble, ascending higher and higher, until no glimpse of his squat figure could be obtained through the dense foliage which enveloped it. 20 Presently his voice was heard in a sort of halloo.

"How much fudder is got for go?"

"How high up are you?" asked Legrand.

"Ebber so fur," replied the negro; "can see de sky fru de top ob de tree."

25 "Never mind the sky, but attend to what I say. Look down the trunk and count the limbs below you on this side. How many limbs have you passed?"

"One, two, tree, four, fibe—I done pass fibe big limb, massa, pon dis side."

30 "Then go one limb higher."

In a few minutes the voice was heard again, announcing that the seventh limb was attained.

"Now, Jup," cried Legrand, evidently much excited, "I want you to work your way out upon that limb as far as you can. If you see anything strange, let me know."

By this time what little doubt I might have entertained of my poor friend's insanity was put finally at rest. I had no alternative but to conclude him stricken with lunacy, and I became seriously anxious about getting him home. While I was pondering upon what was best to be done, Jupiter's voice was again heard.

"Mos feerd for to ventur pon dis limb berry far—'tis dead limb putty much all de way."

"Did you say it was a *dead* limb, Jupiter?" cried Legrand in a quavering voice.

"Yes, massa, him dead as de door-nail—done up for sartain—done departed dis here life."

"What in the name of heaven shall I do?" asked Legrand, seemingly in the greatest distress.

"Do!" said I, glad of an opportunity to interpose a word, "why come home and go to bed. Come now!—that's a fine fellow. It's getting late, and, besides, you remember your promise."

"Jupiter," cried he, without heeding me in the least, "do you hear me?"

"Yes, Massa Will, hear you ebber so plain."

"Try the wood well, then, with your knife, and see if you think it *very* rotten."

"Him rotten, massa, sure nuff," replied the negro in a few moments, "but not so berry rotten as mought be. Mought ventur out leetle way pon de limb by myself, dat's true."

"By yourself!—what do you mean?"

"Why, I mean de bug. 'Tis *berry* hebby bug. Spose I drop him down fuss, and den de limb won't break wid just de weight of one nigger."

"You infernal scoundrel!" cried Legrand, apparently

much relieved, "what do you mean by telling me such nonsense as that? As sure as you let that beetle fall, I'll break your neck. Look here, Jupiter! do you hear me?"

"Yes, massa, needn't hollo at poor nigger dat style."

5 "Well! now listen!—if you will venture out on the limb as far as you think safe, and not let go the beetle, I'll make you a present of a silver dollar as soon as you get down."

"I'm gwine, Massa Will—deed I is," replied the 10 negro very promptly—"mos out to the eend now."

"Out to the end!" here fairly screamed Legrand, "do you say you are out to the end of that limb?"

"Soon be to de eend, massa,—o-o-o-o-oh! Lor-gol-a-marcy! what *is* dis here pon de tree?"

15 "Well!" cried Legrand, highly delighted, "what is it?"

"Why taint noffin but a skull—somebody bin lef him head up de tree, and de crows done gobble ebery bit ob de meat off."

20 "A skull, you say!—very well!—how is it fastened to the limb?—what holds it on?"

"Sure nuff, massa; must look. Why, dis berry curous sarcumstance, pon my word—dare's a great big nail in de skull, what fastens ob it on to de tree."

25 "Well now, Jupiter, do exactly as I tell you—do you hear?"

"Yes, massa."

"Pay attention, then!—find the left eye of the skull."

"Hum! hoo! dat's good! why, dar aint no eye lef at 30 all."

"Curse your stupidity! do you know your right hand from your left?"

"Yes, I nose dat—nose all bout dat—'tis my lef hand what I chops de wood wid."

"To be sure! you are left-handed; and your left eye is on the same side as your left hand. Now, I suppose, you can find the left eye of the skull, or the place where the left eye has been. Have you found it?"

Here was a long pause. At length the negro asked, 5

"Is de lef eye of de skull pon de same side as de lef hand of de skull, too?—cause de skull aint got not a bit ob a hand at all—nebber mind! I got de lef eye now—here de lef eye! what mus do wid it?"

"Let the beetle drop through it, as far as the string 10 will reach—but be careful and not let go your hold of the string."

"All dat done, Massa Will; mighty easy ting for to put de bug fru de hole—look out for him dar below!" 15

During this colloquy no portion of Jupiter's person could be seen; but the beetle, which he had suffered to descend, was now visible at the end of the string, and glistened, like a globe of burnished gold, in the last rays of the setting sun, some of which still faintly illumined the 20 eminence upon which we stood. The *scarabæus* hung quite clear of any branches, and, if allowed to fall, would have fallen at our feet. Legrand immediately took the scythe, and cleared with it a circular space, three or four yards in diameter, just beneath the insect, and, having 25 accomplished this, ordered Jupiter to let go the string and come down from the tree.

Driving a peg, with great nicety, into the ground, at the precise spot where the beetle fell, my friend now produced from his pocket a tape-measure. Fastening one end 30 of this at that point of the trunk of the tree which was nearest the peg, he unrolled it till it reached the peg, and thence farther unrolled it, in the direction already established by the two points of the tree and the peg, for the distance of fifty feet—Jupiter clearing away the brambles with the scythe. At the spot thus attained a second peg was driven, and about this, as a center, a rude circle, about four feet in diameter, described. Taking 5 now a spade himself, and giving one to Jupiter and one to me, Legrand begged us to set about digging as quickly as possible.

To speak the truth, I had no especial relish for such amusement at any time, and, at that particular moment, 10 would most willingly have declined it; for the night was coming on, and I felt much fatigued with the exercise already taken; but I saw no mode of escape, and was fearful of disturbing my poor friend's equanimity by a refusal. Could I have depended, indeed, upon Jupiter's 15 aid, I would have had no hesitation in attempting to get the lunatic home by force; but I was too well assured of the old negro's disposition to hope that he would assist me, under any circumstances, in a personal contest with his master. I made no doubt that the latter had 20 been infected with some of the innumerable Southern superstitions about money buried, and that his fantasy had received confirmation by the finding of the *scarabæus,* or, perhaps, by Jupiter's obstinacy in maintaining it to be "a bug of real gold." A mind disposed to lunacy would 25 readily be led away by such suggestions, especially if chiming in with favorite preconceived ideas; and then I called to mind the poor fellow's speech about the beetle's being "the index of his fortune." Upon the whole, I was sadly vexed and puzzled, but at length I concluded 30 to make a virtue of necessity—to dig with a good will, and thus the sooner to convince the visionary, by ocular demonstration, of the fallacy of the opinions he entertained.

The lanterns having been lit, we all fell to work with a

zeal worthy a more rational cause; and, as the glare fell upon our persons and implements, I could not help thinking how picturesque a group we composed, and how strange and suspicious our labors must have appeared to any interloper who, by chance, might have stumbled upon 5 our whereabouts.

We dug very steadily for two hours. Little was said; and our chief embarrassment lay in the yelpings of the dog, who took exceeding interest in our proceedings. He, at length, became so obstreperous that we grew fear- 10 ful of his giving the alarm to some stragglers in the vicinity; or, rather, this was the apprehension of Legrand; for myself, I should have rejoiced at any interruption which might have enabled me to get the wanderer home. The noise was, at length, very effectually silenced by 15 Jupiter, who, getting out of the hole with a dogged air of deliberation, tied the brute's mouth up with one of his suspenders, and then returned, with a grave chuckle, to his task.

When the time mentioned had expired, we had reached 20 a depth of five feet, and yet no signs of any treasure became manifest. A general pause ensued, and I began to hope that the farce was at an end. Legrand, however, although evidently much disconcerted, wiped his brow thoughtfully and recommenced. We had excavated the 25 entire circle of four feet diameter, and now we slightly enlarged the limit, and went to the farther depth of two feet. Still nothing appeared. The gold-seeker, whom I sincerely pitied, at length clambered from the pit, with the bitterest disappointment imprinted upon every feature, and 30 proceeded, slowly and reluctantly, to put on his coat, which he had thrown off at the beginning of his labor. In the meantime I made no remark. Jupiter, at a signal from his master, began to gather up his tools. This done, and the dog having been unmuzzled, we turned in profound silence towards home.

We had taken, perhaps, a dozen steps in this direction, when, with a loud oath, Legrand strode up to Jupi-
5 ter, and seized him by the collar. The astonished negro opened his eyes and mouth to the fullest extent, let fall the spades, and fell upon his knees.

"You scoundrel," said Legrand, hissing out the syllables from between his clinched teeth—"you infernal
10 black villain!—speak, I tell you!—answer me this instant, without prevarication!—which—which is your left eye?"

"Oh, my golly, Massa Will! aint dis here my lef eye for sartain?" roared the terrified Jupiter, placing
15 his hand upon his *right* organ of vision, and holding it there with a desperate pertinacity, as if in immediate dread of his master's attempt at a gouge.

"I thought so!—I knew it! hurrah!" vociferated Legrand, letting the negro go, and executing a series of
20 curvets and caracoles, much to the astonishment of his valet, who, arising from his knees, looked mutely from his master to myself, and then from myself to his master.

"Come! we must go back," said the latter, "the
25 game's not up yet;" and he again led the way to the tulip-tree.

"Jupiter," said he, when we reached its foot, "come here! was the skull nailed to the limb with the face outward, or with the face to the limb?"

30 "De face was out, massa, so dat de crows could get at de eyes good, widout any trouble."

"Well, then, was it this eye or that through which you dropped the beetle?"—here Legrand touched each of Jupiter's eyes.

"'Twas dis eye, massa—de lef eye—jis as you tell me," and here it was his right eye that the negro indicated.

"That will do—we must try it again."

Here my friend, about whose madness I now saw, or fancied that I saw, certain indications of method, removed the peg which marked the spot where the beetle fell, to a spot about three inches to the westward of its former position. Taking, now, the tape-measure from the nearest point of the trunk to the peg, as before, and continuing the extension in a straight line to the distance of fifty feet, a spot was indicated, removed, by several yards, from the point at which we had been digging.

Around the new position a circle, somewhat larger than in the former instance, was now described, and we again set to work with the spades. I was dreadfully weary, but, scarcely understanding what had occasioned the change in my thoughts, I felt no longer any great aversion from the labor imposed. I had become most unaccountably interested—nay, even excited. Perhaps there was something, amid all the extravagant demeanor of Legrand—some air of forethought, or of deliberation—which impressed me. I dug eagerly, and now and then caught myself actually looking, with something that very much resembled expectation, for the fancied treasure, the vision of which had demented my unfortunate companion. At a period when such vagaries of thought most fully possessed me, and when we had been at work perhaps an hour and a half, we were again interrupted by the violent howlings of the dog. His uneasiness, in the first instance, had been evidently but the result of playfulness or caprice, but he now assumed a bitter and serious tone. Upon Jupiter's again attempting to muzzle him, he made furious resistance, and, leaping into the hole, tore up the mold frantically with his claws. In a few seconds he had uncovered a mass of human bones, forming two complete skeletons, intermingled with several buttons of metal, and what appeared to be the dust of decayed woolen. One or two strokes of a spade upturned the blade of a large Spanish knife, and, as we dug farther, three or four loose pieces of gold and silver coin came to light.

At sight of these the joy of Jupiter could scarcely be restrained, but the countenance of his master wore an air of extreme disappointment. He urged us, however, to continue our exertions, and the words were hardly uttered when I stumbled and fell forward, having caught the toe of my boot in a large ring of iron that lay half buried in the loose earth.

We now worked in earnest, and never did I pass ten minutes of more intense excitement. During this interval we had fairly unearthed an oblong chest of wood, which, from its perfect preservation and wonderful hardness, had plainly been subjected to some mineralizing process—perhaps that of the bichloride of mercury. This box was three feet and a half long, three feet broad, and two and a half feet deep. It was firmly secured by bands of wrought iron, riveted, and forming a kind of trellis-work over the whole. On each side of the chest, near the top, were three rings of iron—six in all—by means of which a firm hold could be obtained by six persons. Our utmost united endeavors served only to disturb the coffer very slightly in its bed. We at once saw the impossibility of removing so great a weight. Luckily, the sole fastenings of the lid consisted of two sliding bolts. These we drew back—trembling and panting with anxiety. In an instant, a treasure of incalculable value lay gleaming before us. As the rays of the lanterns fell within the pit, there flashed upwards, from a confused heap of gold and of jewels, a glow and a glare that absolutely dazzled our eyes.

I shall not pretend to describe the feelings with which I gazed. Amazement was, of course, predominant. Legrand appeared exhausted with excitement, and spoke very few words. Jupiter's countenance wore, for some minutes, as deadly a pallor as it is possible, in the nature of things, for any negro's visage to assume. He seemed stupefied—thunderstricken. Presently he fell upon his knees in the pit, and, burying his naked arms up to the elbows in gold, let them there remain, as if enjoying the luxury of a bath. At length, with a deep sigh, he exclaimed, as if in a soliloquy:

"And dis all cum ob de goole-bug! de putty goole-bug! de poor little goole-bug, what I boosed in dat sabage kind ob style! Ain't you shamed ob yourself, nigger?—answer me dat!"

It became necessary, at last, that I should arouse both master and valet to the expediency of removing the treasure. It was growing late, and it behooved us to make exertion, that we might get everything housed before daylight. It was difficult to say what should be done, and much time was spent in deliberation—so confused were the ideas of all. We finally lightened the box by removing two-thirds of its contents, when we were enabled, with some trouble, to raise it from the hole. The articles taken out were deposited among the brambles, and the dog left to guard them, with strict orders from Jupiter neither, upon any pretense, to stir from the spot, nor to open his mouth until our return. We then hurriedly made for home with the chest; reaching the hut in safety, but after excessive toil, at one o'clock in the morning. Worn out as we were, it was not in human nature to do more just now. We rested until two, and had supper; starting for the hills immediately afterwards, armed with three stout sacks, which by good luck were upon the premises.

A little before four we arrived at the pit, divided the remainder of the booty, as equally as might be, among us, and, leaving the holes unfilled, again set out for the hut, at which, for the second time, we deposited our golden
5 burdens, just as the first streaks of the dawn gleamed from over the treetops in the east.

We were now thoroughly broken down; but the intense excitement of the time denied us repose. After an unquiet slumber of some three or four hours' duration, we
10 arose, as if by preconcert, to make examination of our treasure.

The chest had been full to the brim, and we spent the whole day, and the greater part of the next night, in a scrutiny of its contents. There had been nothing like
15 order or arrangement. Everything had been heaped in promiscuously. Having assorted all with care, we found ourselves possessed of even vaster wealth than we had at first supposed. In coin there was rather more than four hundred and fifty thousand dollars: estimating the value
20 of the pieces, as accurately as we could, by the tables of the period. There was not a particle of silver. All was gold of antique date and of great variety: French, Spanish, and German money, with a few English guineas, and some counters, of which we had never seen specimens
25 before. There were several very large and heavy coins, so worn that we could make nothing of their inscriptions. There was no American money. The value of the jewels we found more difficulty in estimating. There were diamonds—some of them exceedingly large and fine—a hun-
30 dred and ten in all, and not one of them small; eighteen rubies of remarkable brilliancy; three hundred and ten emeralds, all very beautiful; and twenty-one sapphires, with an opal. These stones had all been broken from their settings, and thrown loose in the chest. The settings

themselves, which we picked out from among the other gold, appeared to have been beaten up with hammers, as if to prevent identification. Besides all this, there was a vast quantity of solid gold ornaments: nearly two hundred massive finger and ear rings; rich chains—thirty 5 of these, if I remember; eighty-three very large and heavy crucifixes; five gold censers of great value; a prodigious golden punch-bowl, ornamented with richly chased vine-leaves and Bacchanalian figures; with two sword-handles exquisitely embossed, and many other smaller articles 10 which I cannot recollect. The weight of these valuables exceeded three hundred and fifty pounds avoirdupois; and in this estimate I have not included one hundred and ninety-seven superb gold watches; three of the number being worth each five hundred dollars, if one. Many of 15 them were very old, and as timekeepers valueless, the works having suffered more or less from corrosion; but all were richly jeweled and in cases of great worth. We estimated the entire contents of the chest, that night, at a million and a half of dollars; and, upon the subse- 20 quent disposal of the trinkets and jewels (a few being retained for our own use), it was found that we had greatly undervalued the treasure.

When, at length, we had concluded our examination, and the intense excitement of the time had in some meas- 25 ure subsided, Legrand, who saw that I was dying with impatience for a solution of this most extraordinary riddle, entered into a full detail of all the circumstances connected with it.

"You remember," said he, "the night when I handed 30 you the rough sketch I had made of the *scarabæus*. You recollect also, that I became quite vexed at you for insisting that my drawing resembled a death's-head. When you first made this assertion I thought you were jesting;

but afterwards I called to mind the peculiar spots on the back of the insect, and admitted to myself that your remark had some little foundation in fact. Still, the sneer at my graphic powers irritated me—for I am considered 5 a good artist—and, therefore, when you handed me the scrap of parchment, I was about to crumple it up and throw it angrily into the fire."

"The scrap of paper, you mean," said I.

"No: it had much of the appearance of paper, and at 10 first I supposed it to be such, but when I came to draw upon it, I discovered it, at once, to be a piece of very thin parchment. It was quite dirty, you remember. Well, as I was in the very act of crumpling it up, my glance fell upon the sketch at which you had been look- 15 ing, and you may imagine my astonishment when I perceived, in fact, the figure of a death's-head just where, it seemed to me, I had made the drawing of the beetle. For a moment I was too much amazed to think with accuracy. I knew that my design was very different in 20 detail from this—although there was a certain similarity in general outline. Presently I took a candle and, seating myself at the other side of the room, proceeded to scrutinize the parchment more closely. Upon turning it over, I saw my own sketch upon the reverse, just as I had made it. 25 My first idea, now, was mere surprise at the really remarkable similarity of outline—at the singular coincidence involved in the fact that, unknown to me, there should have been a skull upon the other side of the parchment, immediately beneath my figure of the *scarabæus,* and that 30 this skull, not only in outline, but in size, should so closely resemble my drawing. I say the singularity of this coincidence absolutely stupefied me for a time. This is the usual effect of such coincidences. The mind struggles to establish a connection—a sequence of cause and effect—and, being unable to do so, suffers a species of temporary paralysis. But, when I recovered from this stupor, there dawned upon me gradually a conviction which startled me even far more than the coincidence. I began distinctly, positively, to remember that there had been 5 *no* drawing on the parchment when I made my sketch of the *scarabæus*. I became perfectly certain of this; for I recollected turning up first one side and then the other, in search of the cleanest spot. Had the skull been then there, of course I could not have failed to notice it. Here was 10 indeed a mystery which I felt it impossible to explain; but, even at that early moment, there seemed to glimmer, faintly, within the most remote and secret chambers of my intellect, a glow-worm-like conception of that truth which last night's adventure brought to so magnificent a demon- 15 stration. I arose at once, and, putting the parchment securely away, dismissed all farther reflection until I should be alone.

"When you had gone, and when Jupiter was fast asleep, I betook myself to a more methodical investiga- 20 tion of the affair. In the first place I considered the manner in which the parchment had come into my possession. The spot where we discovered the *scarabæus* was on the coast of the mainland, about a mile eastward of the island, and but a short distance above high- 25 water mark. Upon my taking hold of it, it gave me a sharp bite, which caused me to let it drop. Jupiter, with his accustomed caution, before seizing the insect, which had flown towards him, looked about him for a leaf, or something of that nature, by which to take hold of it. 30 It was at this moment that his eyes, and mine also, fell upon the scrap of parchment, which I then supposed to be paper. It was lying half-buried in the sand, a corner sticking up. Near the spot where we found it, I observed the remnants of the hull of what appeared to have been a ship's long boat. The wreck seemed to have been there for a very great while; for the resemblance to boat timbers could scarcely be traced.

5 "Well, Jupiter picked up the parchment, wrapped the beetle in it, and gave it to me. Soon afterwards we turned to go home, and on the way met Lieutenant G——. I showed him the insect, and he begged me to let him take it to the fort. On my consenting, he thrust 10 it forthwith into his waistcoat pocket, without the parchment in which it had been wrapped, and which I had continued to hold in my hand during his inspection. Perhaps he dreaded my changing my mind, and thought it best to make sure of the prize at once—you know how 15 enthusiastic he is on all subjects connected with Natural History. At the same time, without being conscious of it, I must have deposited the parchment in my own pocket.

"You remember that when I went to the table, for the purpose of making a sketch of the beetle, I found no 20 paper where it was usually kept. I looked in the drawer, and found none there. I searched my pockets, hoping to find an old letter, and then my hand fell upon the parchment. I thus detail the precise mode in which it came into my possession; for the circumstances impressed me 25 with peculiar force.

"No doubt you will think me fanciful—but I had already established a kind of *connection*. I had put together two links of a great chain. There was a boat lying on a seacoast, and not far from the boat was a 30 parchment—*not a paper*—with a skull depicted on it. You will, of course, ask 'where is the connection?' I reply that the skull, or death's-head, is the well-known emblem of the pirate. The flag of the death's-head is hoisted in all engagements.

"I have said that the scrap was parchment, and not paper. Parchment is durable—almost imperishable. Matters of little moment are rarely consigned to parchment; since, for the mere ordinary purposes of drawing or writing, it is not nearly so well adapted as paper. 5 This reflection suggested some meaning—some relevancy —in the death's-head. I did not fail to observe, also, the *form* of the parchment. Although one of its corners had been, by some accident, destroyed, it could be seen that the original form was oblong. It was just such a 10 slip, indeed, as might have been chosen for a memorandum—for a record of something to be long remembered and carefully preserved."

"But," I interposed, "you say that the skull was *not* upon the parchment when you made the drawing of the 15 beetle. How then do you trace any connection between the boat and the skull—since this latter, according to your own admission, must have been designed (God only knows how or by whom) at some period subsequent to your sketching the *scarabæus?*" 20

"Ah, hereupon turns the whole mystery; although the secret, at this point, I had comparatively little difficulty in solving. My steps were sure, and could afford but a single result. I reasoned, for example, thus: When I drew the *scarabæus,* there was no skull apparent on the 25 parchment. When I had completed the drawing I gave it to you, and observed you narrowly until you returned it. *You*, therefore, did not design the skull, and no one else was present to do it. Then it was not done by human agency. And nevertheless it was done. 30

"At this stage of my reflections I endeavored to remember, and *did* remember, with entire distinctness, every incident which occurred about the period in question. The weather was chilly (O rare and happy accident!), and a fire was blazing on the hearth. I was heated with exercise and sat near the table. You, however, had drawn a chair close to the chimney. Just as I placed the parchment in your hand, and as you were in the act of inspecting it, Wolf, the Newfoundland, entered, and leaped upon your shoulders. With your left hand you caressed him and kept him off, while your right, holding the parchment, was permitted to fall listlessly between your knees, and in close proximity to the fire. At one moment I thought the blaze had caught it, and was about to caution you, but, before I could speak, you had withdrawn it, and were engaged in its examination. When I considered all these particulars, I doubted not for a moment that *heat* had been the agent in bringing to light, on the parchment, the skull which I saw designed on it. You are well aware that chemical preparations exist, and have existed time out of mind, by means of which it is possible to write on either paper or vellum, so that the characters shall become visible only when subjected to the action of fire. Zaffer, digested in *aqua regia,* and diluted with four times its weight of water, is sometimes employed; a green tint results. The regulus of cobalt, dissolved in spirit of niter, gives a red. These colors disappear at longer or shorter intervals after the material written upon cools, but again become apparent upon the re-application of heat.

"I now scrutinized the death's-head with care. Its outer edges—the edges of the drawing nearest the edge of the vellum—were far more *distinct* than the others. It was clear that the action of the caloric had been imperfect or unequal. I immediately kindled a fire, and subjected every portion of the parchment to a glowing heat. At first, the only effect was the strengthening of the faint lines in the skull; but, on persevering in the experiment, there became visible at the corner of the slip, diagonally opposite to the spot in which the death's-head was delineated, the figure of what I at first supposed to be a goat. A closer scrutiny, however, satisfied me that it was intended for a kid." 5

"Ha! ha!" said I, "to be sure I have no right to laugh at you—a million and a half of money is too serious a matter for mirth—but you are not about to establish a third link in your chain: you will not find any especial connection between your pirates and a goat; pirates, you know, have nothing to do with goats; they appertain to the farming interest." 10

"But I have just said that the figure was *not* that of a goat."

"Well, a kid, then—pretty much the same thing." 15

"Pretty much, but not altogether," said Legrand. "You may have heard of one *Captain* Kidd. I at once looked on the figure of the animal as a kind of punning or hieroglyphical signature. I say signature; because its position on the vellum suggested this idea. The death's-head at the corner diagonally opposite had, in the same manner, the air of a stamp, or seal. But I was sorely put out by the absence of all else—of the body to my imagined instrument—of the text for my context." 20

"I presume you expected to find a letter between the stamp and the signature." 25

"Something of that kind. The fact is, I felt irresistibly impressed with a presentiment of some vast good fortune impending. I can scarcely say why. Perhaps, after all, it was rather a desire than an actual belief;—but do you know that Jupiter's silly words, about the bug being of solid gold, had a remarkable effect on my fancy? And then the series of accidents and coincidences—these were so *very* extraordinary. Do you observe how mere 30

an accident it was that these events should have occurred on the *sole* day of all the year in which it has been, or may be, sufficiently cool for fire, and that without the fire, or without the intervention of the dog at the precise
5 moment in which he appeared, I should never have become aware of the death's-head, and so never the possessor of the treasure?"

"But proceed—I am all impatience."

"Well; you have heard, of course, the many stories
10 current—the thousand vague rumors afloat about money buried, somewhere on the Atlantic coast, by Kidd and his associates. These rumors must have had some foundation in fact. And that the rumors have existed so long and so continuously, could have resulted, it appeared to
15 me, only from the circumstance of the buried treasure still *remaining* entombed. Had Kidd concealed his plunder for a time, and afterwards reclaimed it, the rumors would scarcely have reached us in their present unvarying form. You will observe that the stories told are all
20 about money-seekers, not about money-finders. Had the pirate recovered his money, there the affair would have dropped. It seemed to me that some accident—say the loss of a memorandum indicating its locality—had deprived him of the means of recovering it, and that this
25 accident had become known to his followers, who otherwise might never have heard that treasure had been concealed at all, and who, busying themselves in vain, because unguided, attempts to regain it, had given first birth, and then universal currency, to the reports which are
30 now so common. Have you ever heard of any important treasure being unearthed along the coast?"

"Never."

"But that Kidd's accumulations were immense is well known. I took it for granted, therefore, that the earth still held them; and you will scarcely be surprised when I tell you that I felt a hope, nearly amounting to certainty, that the parchment so strangely found involved a lost record of the place of deposit."

"But how did you proceed?"

"I held the vellum again to the fire, after increasing the heat, but nothing appeared. I now thought it possible that the coating of dirt might have something to do with the failure, so I carefully rinsed the parchment by pouring warm water over it, and, having done this, I placed it in a tin pan, with the skull downwards, and put the pan upon a furnace of lighted charcoal. In a few minutes, the pan having become thoroughly heated, I removed the slip, and, to my inexpressible joy, found it spotted, in several places, with what appeared to be figures arranged in lines. Again I placed it in the pan, and suffered it to remain another minute. Upon taking it off, the whole was just as you see it now."

Here Legrand, having reheated the parchment, submitted it to my inspection. The following characters were rudely traced, in a red tint, between the death's-head and the goat:—

53‡‡†305))6*;4826)4‡.)4‡);806*;48†8¶60))85;;]8*;:‡*8†83(88)5*†;
46(;88*96*?;8)*‡(;485);5*†2:*‡(;4956*2(5*—4)8¶8*;4069285);)6†8)
4‡‡;1(‡9;48081;8:8‡1;48†85;4)485†528806*81(‡9;48;(88;4(‡?34;48)
4‡;161;:188;‡?;

"But," said I, returning him the slip, "I am as much in the dark as ever. Were all the jewels of Golconda awaiting me on my solution of this enigma, I am quite sure that I should be unable to earn them."

"And yet," said Legrand, "the solution is by no means so difficult as you might be led to imagine from the first hasty inspection of the characters. These characters, as any one might readily guess, form a cipher—that is to say, they convey a meaning; but then, from what is known of Kidd, I could not suppose him capable of constructing any of the more abstruse cryptographs. I made 5 up my mind, at once, that this was of a simple species—such, however, as would appear, to the crude intellect of the sailor, absolutely insoluble without the key."

"And you really solved it?"

"Readily; I have solved others of an abstruseness 10 ten thousand times greater. Circumstances, and a certain bias of mind, have led me to take interest in such riddles, and it may well be doubted whether human ingenuity can construct an enigma of the kind which human ingenuity may not, by proper application, resolve. In fact, having 15 once established connected and legible characters, I scarcely gave a thought to the mere difficulty of developing their import.

"In the present case—indeed in all cases of secret writing—the first question regards the *language* of the 20 cipher; for the principles of solution, so far, especially, as the more simple ciphers are concerned, depend on, and are varied by, the genius of the particular idiom. In general, there is no alternative but experiment (directed by probabilities) of every tongue known to him who 25 attempts the solution, until the true one be attained. But, with the cipher now before us, all difficulty is removed by the signature. The pun upon the word 'Kidd' is appreciable in no other language than the English. But for this consideration I should have begun my attempts with 30 the Spanish and French, as the tongues in which a secret of this kind would most naturally have been written by a pirate of the Spanish main. As it was, I assumed the cryptograph to be English.

"You observe there are no divisions between the words.

Had there been divisions, the task would have been comparatively easy. In such case I should have commenced with a collation and analysis of the shorter words, and, had a word of a single letter occurred, as is most likely (*a* or *I*, for example), I should have considered the solu- 5
tion as assured. But, there being no division, my first step was to ascertain the predominant letters, as well as the least frequent. Counting all, I constructed a table, thus:

Of the character		there are		
	8	there are	33	10
	;	"	26	
	4	"	19	
	‡)	"	16	
	*	"	13	
	5	"	12	15
	6	"	11	
	†1	"	8	
	0	"	6	
	92	"	5	
	:3	"	4	20
	?	"	3	
	¶	"	2	
	—.	"	1	

"Now, in English, the letter which most frequently occurs is *e*. Afterwards the succession runs thus: *a o i d h* 25
n r s t u y c f g l m w b k p q x z. *E* predominates, however, so remarkably that an individual sentence of any length is rarely seen, in which it is not the prevailing character.

"Here, then, we have, in the very beginning, the 30
groundwork for something more than a mere guess. The general use which may be made of the table is obvious—but, in this particular cipher, we shall only very partially require its aid. As our predominant character is 8, we will commence by assuming it as the *e* of the natural 35

alphabet. To verify the supposition, let us observe if the 8 be seen often in couples—for *e* is doubled with great frequency in English—in such words, for example, as 'meet,' 'fleet,' 'speed,' 'seen,' 'been,' 'agree,' etc. In
5 the present instance we see it doubled no less than five times, although the cryptograph is brief.

"Let us assume 8, then, as *e*. Now, of all *words* in the language, 'the' is most usual; let us see, therefore, whether there are not repetitions of any three char-
10 acters, in the same order of collocation, the last of them being 8. If we discover repetitions of such letters, so arranged, they will most probably represent the word 'the.' On inspection, we find no less than seven such arrangements, the characters being ;48. We may, there-
15 fore, assume that the semicolon represents *t,* that 4 represents *h,* and that 8 represents *e*—the last being now well confirmed. Thus a great step has been taken.

"But having established a single word, we are enabled to establish a vastly important point; that is to say,
20 several commencements and terminations of other words. Let us refer, for example, to the last instance but one, in which the combination ;48 occurs—not far from the end of the cipher. We know that the semicolon immediately ensuing is the commencement of a word, and, of
25 the six characters succeeding this 'the,' we are cognizant of no less than five. Let us set these characters down, thus, by the letters we know them to represent, leaving a space for the unknown—

t eeth.

30 "Here we are enabled, at once, to discard the '*th,*' as forming no portion of the word commencing with the first *t;* since, by experiment of the entire alphabet for a letter adapted to the vacancy, we perceive that no word

can be formed of which this *th* can be a part. We are thus narrowed into

t ee,

and, going through the alphabet, if necessary, as before, we arrive at the word 'tree' as the sole possible reading. We 5 thus gain another letter, *r*, represented by (, with the words 'the tree' in juxtaposition.

"Looking beyond these words, for a short distance, we again see the combination ;48, and employ it by way of *termination* to what immediately precedes. We have 10 thus this arrangement:

the tree ;4(‡?34 the,

or, substituting the natural letters, where known, it reads thus:

the tree thr‡?3h the. 15

"Now, if, in place of the unknown characters, we leave blank spaces, or substitute dots, we read thus:

the tree thr... h the,

when the word '*through*' makes itself evident at once. But this discovery gives us three new letters, *o*, *u*, and *g*, 20 represented by ‡ ? and 3.

"Looking now, narrowly, through the cipher for combinations of known characters, we find not very far from the beginning, this arrangement,

83(88, or egree, 25

which, plainly, is the conclusion of the word 'degree,' and gives us another letter, d, represented by †.

"Four letters beyond the word 'degree,' we perceive the combination

;46(;88*

"Translating the known characters, and representing
5 the unknown by dots, as before, we read thus:

th . rtee .

an arrangement immediately suggestive of the word 'thirteen,' and again furnishing us with two new characters, *i* and *n*, represented by 6 and *.
10 "Referring, now, to the beginning of the cryptograph, we find the combination,

53‡‡†.

"Translating, as before, we obtain

. good,

15 which assures us that the first letter is *A*, and that the first two words are 'A good.'

"To avoid confusion, it is now time that we arrange our key, as far as discovered, in a tabular form. It will stand thus:

20 5 represents a
† " d
8 " e
3 " g
4 " h
25 6 " i
* " n
‡ " o
(" r
; " t

"We have, therefore, no less than ten of the most important letters represented, and it will be unnecessary to proceed with the details of the solution. I have said enough to convince you that ciphers of this nature are readily soluble, and to give you some insight into the rationale of their development. But be assured that the specimen before us appertains to the very simplest species of cryptograph. It now only remains to give you the full translation of the characters upon the parchment, as unriddled. Here it is:

"'A good glass in the bishop's hostel in the devil's seat twenty one degrees and thirteen minutes north-east and by north main branch seventh limb east side shoot from the left eye of the death's-head a bee-line from the tree through the shot fifty feet out.'"

"But," said I, "the enigma seems still in as bad a condition as ever. How is it possible to extort a meaning from all this jargon about 'devil's seats,' 'death's-heads,' and 'bishop's hotels'?"

"I confess," replied Legrand, "that the matter still wears a serious aspect, when regarded with a casual glance. My first endeavor was to divide the sentence into the natural division intended by the cryptographist."

"You mean, to punctuate it?"

"Something of that kind."

"But how was it possible to effect this?"

"I reflected that it had been a *point* with the writer to run his words together without division, so as to increase the difficulty of solution. Now, a not over-acute man, in pursuing such an object, would be nearly certain to overdo the matter. When, in the course of his composition, he arrived at a break in his subject which would naturally require a pause, or a point, he would be exceedingly apt to run his characters, at this place, more than usually close together. If you will observe the MS., in the present instance, you will easily detect five such cases of unusual 5 crowding. Acting on this hint, I made the division thus:

"'A good glass in the Bishop's hostel in the Devil's seat —twenty-one degrees and thirteen minutes—north-east and by north—main branch seventh limb east side—shoot from the left eye of the death's-head—a bee-line from the tree through 10 *the shot fifty feet out.'"*

"Even this division," said I, "leaves me still in the dark."

"It left me also in the dark," replied Legrand, "for a few days; during which I made diligent inquiry, in the 15 neighborhood of Sullivan's Island, for any building which went by the name of the 'Bishop's Hotel'; for, of course, I dropped the obsolete word 'hostel.' Gaining no information on the subject, I was on the point of extending my sphere of search, and proceeding in a more systematic man- 20 ner, when one morning it entered into my head, quite suddenly, that this 'Bishop's Hostel' might have some reference to an old family, of the name of Bessop, which, time out of mind, had held possession of an ancient manor-house, about four miles to the northward of the 25 island. I accordingly went over to the plantation, and reinstituted my inquiries among the older negroes of the place. At length one of the most aged of the women said that she had heard of such a place as *Bessop's Castle,* and thought that she could guide me to it, but that it was 30 not a castle, nor a tavern, but a high rock.

"I offered to pay her well for her trouble, and, after some demur, she consented to accompany me to the spot. We found it without much difficulty, when, dismissing her, I proceeded to examine the place. The 'castle' consisted of an irregular assemblage of cliffs and rocks—one of the latter being quite remarkable for its height as well as for its insulated and artificial appearance. I clambered to its apex, and then felt much at a loss as to what should be next done. 5

"While I was busied in reflection, my eyes fell on a narrow ledge in the eastern face of the rock, perhaps a yard below the summit upon which I stood. This ledge projected about eighteen inches, and was not more 10 than a foot wide, while a niche in the cliff just above it gave it a rude resemblance to one of the hollow-backed chairs used by our ancestors. I made no doubt that here was the 'devil's seat' alluded to in the MS., and now I seemed to grasp the full secret of the riddle. 15

"The 'good glass,' I knew, could have reference to nothing but a telescope; for the word 'glass' is rarely employed in any other sense by seamen. Now here, I at once saw, was a telescope to be used, and a definite point of view, *admitting no variation,* from which to use it. 20 Nor did I hesitate to believe that the phrases, 'twenty-one degrees and thirteen minutes,' and 'north-east and by north,' were intended as directions for the leveling of the glass. Greatly excited by these discoveries, I hurried home, procured a telescope, and returned to the rock. 25

"I let myself down to the ledge, and found that it was impossible to retain a seat on it unless in one particular position. This fact confirmed my preconceived idea. I proceeded to use the glass. Of course, the 'twenty-one degrees and thirteen minutes' could allude 30 to nothing but elevation above the visible horizon, since the horizontal direction was clearly indicated by the words, 'north-east and by north.' This latter direction I at once established by means of a pocket-compass; then,

pointing the glass as nearly at an angle of twenty-one degrees of elevation as I could do it by guess, I moved it cautiously up or down, until my attention was arrested by a circular rift or opening in the foliage of a large tree
5 that overtopped its fellows in the distance. In the center of this rift I perceived a white spot, but could not, at first, distinguish what it was. Adjusting the focus of the telescope, I again looked, and now made it out to be a human skull.

10 "On this discovery I was so sanguine as to consider the enigma solved; for the phrase 'main branch, seventh limb, east side,' could refer only to the position of the skull on the tree, while 'shoot from the left eye of the death's-head' admitted, also, of but one interpretation, in regard
15 to a search for buried treasure. I perceived that the design was to drop a bullet from the left eye of the skull, and that a bee-line, or, in other words, a straight line, drawn from the nearest point of the trunk through 'the shot' (or the spot where the bullet fell), and thence
20 extended to a distance of fifty feet, would indicate a definite point—and beneath this point I thought it at least *possible* that a deposit of value lay concealed."

"All this," I said, "is exceedingly clear, and, although ingenious, still simple and explicit. When you
25 left the Bishop's Hotel, what then?"

"Why, having carefully taken the bearings of the tree, I turned homewards. The instant that I left 'the devil's seat,' however, the circular rift vanished; nor could I get a glimpse of it afterwards, turn as I would. What
30 seems to me the chief ingenuity in this whole business, is the fact (for repeated experiment has convinced me it *is* a fact) that the circular opening in question is visible from no other attainable point of view than that afforded by the narrow ledge on the face of the rock.

"In this expedition to the 'Bishop's Hotel' I had been attended by Jupiter, who had no doubt observed, for some weeks past, the abstraction of my demeanor, and took special care not to leave me alone. But on the next day, getting up very early, I contrived to give him the slip, and went into the hills in search of the tree. After much toil I found it. When I came home at night my valet proposed to give me a flogging. With the rest of the adventure I believe you are as well acquainted as myself."

"I suppose," said I, "you missed the spot, in the first attempt at digging, through Jupiter's stupidity in letting the bug fall through the right instead of through the left eye of the skull."

"Precisely. This mistake made a difference of about two inches and a half in the 'shot'—that is to say, in the position of the peg nearest the tree; and had the treasure been *beneath* the 'shot,' the error would have been of little moment; but 'the shot,' together with the nearest point of the tree, were merely two points for the esablishment of a line of direction; of course the error, however trivial in the beginning, increased as we proceeded with the line, and, by the time we had gone fifty feet, threw us quite off the scent. But for my deep-seated convictions that treasure was here somewhere actually buried, we might have had all our labor in vain."

"I presume the fancy of the *skull*—of letting fall a bullet through the skull's eye—was suggested to Kidd by the piratical flag. No doubt he felt a kind of poetical consistency in recovering his money through this ominous insignium."

"Perhaps so; still, I cannot help thinking that common sense had quite as much to do with the matter as poetical consistency. To be visible from the Devil's seat, it was necessary that the object, if small, should be *white;* and there is nothing like your human skull for retaining and even increasing its whiteness under exposure to all vicissitudes of weather."

5 "But your grandiloquence, and your conduct in swinging the beetle—how excessively odd! I was sure you were mad. And why did you insist on letting fall the bug, instead of a bullet, from the skull?"

"Why, to be frank, I felt somewhat annoyed by 10 your evident suspicions touching my sanity, and so resolved to punish you quietly, in my own way, by a little bit of sober mystification. For this reason I swung the beetle, and for this reason I let it fall from the tree. An observation of yours about its great weight suggested the latter 15 idea."

"Yes, I perceive; and now there is only one point which puzzles me. What are we to make of the skeletons found in the hole?"

"That is a question I am no more able to answer 20 than yourself. There seems, however, only one plausible way of accounting for them—and yet it is dreadful to believe in such atrocity as my suggestion would imply. It is clear that Kidd—if Kidd indeed secreted this treasure, which I doubt not—it is clear that he must have had 25 assistance in the labor. But, the worst of this labor concluded, he may have thought it expedient to remove all participants in his secret. Perhaps a couple of blows with a mattock were sufficient, while his coadjutors were busy in the pit; perhaps it required a dozen—who shall tell?"

ETHAN BRAND *

A CHAPTER FROM AN ABORTIVE ROMANCE

By NATHANIEL HAWTHORNE

Bartram the lime-burner, a rough, heavy-looking man, begrimed with charcoal, sat watching his kiln, at nightfall, while his little son played at building houses with the scattered fragments of marble, when, on the hill-side below them, they heard a roar of laughter, not mirth- 5 ful, but slow, and even solemn, like a wind shaking the boughs of the forest.

"Father, what is that?" asked the little boy, leaving his play, and pressing betwixt his father's knees.

"O, some drunken man, I suppose," answered the 10 lime-burner; "some merry fellow from the bar-room in the village, who dared not laugh loud enough within doors, lest he should blow the roof of the house off. So here he is, shaking his jolly sides at the foot of Graylock."

"But, father," said the child, more sensitive than 15 the obtuse, middle-aged clown, "he does not laugh like a man that is glad. So the noise frightens me!"

"Don't be a fool, child!" cried his father, gruffly. "You will never make a man, I do believe; there is too

* Nathaniel Hawthorne (1804-1864), American novelist, best known, perhaps, for his series of short stories, *Twice-Told Tales,* in which this tale was included, and *Mosses from an Old Manse,* and for his novels, *The Scarlet Letter*, and *The House of the Seven Gables.* This story was published in 1851. See also pp. 39-45, 47-50, 54, 62, 64-65.

much of your mother in you. I have known the rustling of a leaf startle you. Hark! Here comes the merry fellow now. You shall see that there is no harm in him."

5 Bartram and his little son, while they were talking thus, sat watching the same lime-kiln that had been the scene of Ethan Brand's solitary and meditative life, before he began his search for the Unpardonable Sin. Many years, as we have seen, had now elapsed, since that por-
10 tentous night when the IDEA was first developed. The kiln, however, on the mountain-side, stood unimpaired, and was in nothing changed since he had thrown his dark thoughts into the intense glow of its furnace, and melted them, as it were, into the one thought that took
15 possession of his life. It was a rude, round, towerlike structure, about twenty feet high, heavily built of rough stones, and with a hillock of earth heaped about the larger part of its circumference; so that the blocks and fragments of marble might be drawn by cart-loads, and thrown
20 in at the top. There was an opening at the bottom of the tower like an oven-mouth, but large enough to admit a man in a stooping posture, and provided with a massive iron door. With the smoke and jets of flame issuing from the chinks and crevices of this door, which seemed
25 to give admittance into the hillside, it resembled nothing so much as the private entrance to the infernal regions, which the shepherds of the Delectable Mountains were accustomed to show to pilgrims.

There are many such lime-kilns in that tract of coun-
30 try, for the purpose of burning the white marble which composes a large part of the substance of the hills. Some of them, built years ago, and long deserted, with weeds growing in the vacant round of the interior, which is open to the sky, and grass and wildflowers rooting themselves

into the chinks of the stones, look already like relics of antiquity, and may yet be overspread with the lichens of centuries to come. Others, where the lime-burner still feeds his daily and night-long fire, afford points of interest to the wanderer among the hills, who seats himself on a log of wood or a fragment of marble, to hold a chat with the solitary man. It is a lonesome, and, when the character is inclined to thought, may be an intensely thoughtful occupation; as it proved in the case of Ethan Brand, who had mused to such strange purpose, in days gone by, while the fire in this very kiln was burning.

The man who now watched the fire was of a different order, and troubled himself with no thoughts save the very few that were requisite to his business. At frequent intervals, he flung back the clashing weight of the iron door, and, turning his face from the insufferable glare, thrust in huge logs of oak, or stirred the immense brands with a long pole. Within the furnace were seen the curling and riotous flames, and the burning marble, almost molten with the intensity of heat; while without, the reflection of the fire quivered on the dark intricacy of the surrounding forest, and showed in the foreground a bright and ruddy little picture of the hut, the spring beside its door, the athletic and coal-begrimed figure of the lime-burner, and the half-frightened child, shrinking into the protection of his father's shadow. And when again the iron door was closed, then reappeared the tender light of the half-full moon, which vainly strove to trace out the indistinct shapes of the neighboring mountains; and, in the upper sky, there was a flitting congregation of clouds, still faintly tinged with the rosy sunset, though thus far down into the valley the sunshine had vanished long and long ago.

The little boy now crept still closer to his father, as footsteps were heard ascending the hillside, and a human form thrust aside the bushes that clustered beneath the trees.

5 "Halloo! who is it?" cried the lime-burner, vexed at his son's timidity, yet half infected by it. "Come forward, and show yourself, like a man, or I'll fling this chunk of marble at your head!"

"You offer me a rough welcome," said a gloomy voice, 10 as the unknown man drew nigh. "Yet I neither claim nor desire a kinder one, even at my own fireside."

To obtain a distincter view, Bartram threw open the iron door of the kiln, whence immediately issued a gush of fierce light, that smote full upon the stranger's face 15 and figure. To a careless eye there appeared nothing very remarkable in his aspect, which was that of a man in a coarse, brown, country-made suit of clothes, tall and thin, with the staff and heavy shoes of a wayfarer. As he advanced, he fixed his eyes—which were very bright— 20 intently upon the brightness of the furnace, as if he beheld, or expected to behold, some object worthy of note within it.

"Good evening, stranger," said the lime-burner; "whence come you, so late in the day?"

25 "I come from my search," answered the wayfarer; "for, at last, it is finished."

"Drunk!—or crazy!" muttered Bartram to himself. "I shall have trouble with the fellow. The sooner I drive him away, the better."

30 The little boy, all in a tremble, whispered to his father, and begged him to shut the door of the kiln, so that there might not be so much light; for that there was something in the man's face which he was afraid to look at, yet could not look away from. And, indeed, even

the lime-burner's dull and torpid sense began to be impressed by an indescribable something in that thin, rugged, thoughtful visage, with the grizzled hair hanging wildly about it, and those deeply-sunken eyes, which gleamed like fires within the entrance of a mysterious cavern. 5
But, as he closed the door, the stranger turned towards him, and spoke in a quiet, familiar way, that made Bartram feel as if he were a sane and sensible man, after all.

"Your task draws to an end, I see," said he. "This 10
marble has already been burning three days. A few hours more will convert the stone to lime."

"Why, who are you?" exclaimed the lime-burner. "You seem as well acquainted with my business as I am myself." 15

"And well I may be," said the stranger; "for I followed the same craft many a long year, and here, too, on this very spot. But you are a newcomer in these parts. Did you never hear of Ethan Brand?"

"The man that went in search of the Unpardonable 20
Sin?" asked Bartram, with a laugh.

"The same," answered the stranger. "He has found what he sought, and therefore he comes back again."

"What! then you are Ethan Brand himself?" cried the lime-burner, in amazement. "I am a newcomer here, 25
as you say, and they call it eighteen years since you left the foot of Graylock. But, I can tell you, the good folks still talk about Ethan Brand, in the village yonder, and what a strange errand took him away from his lime-kiln. Well, and so you have found the Unpardonable 30
Sin?"

"Even so!" said the stranger, calmly.

"If the question is a fair one," proceeded Bartram, "where might it be?"

Ethan Brand laid his finger on his own heart.

"Here!" replied he.

And then, without mirth in his countenance, but as if moved by an involuntary recognition of the infinite 5 absurdity of seeking throughout the world for what was the closest of all things to himself, and looking into every heart, save his own, for what was hidden in no other breast, he broke into a laugh of scorn. It was the same slow, heavy laugh that had almost appalled the lime-10 burner when it heralded the wayfarer's approach.

The solitary mountain-side was made dismal by it. Laughter, when out of place, mistimed, or bursting forth from a disordered state of feeling, may be the most terrible modulation of the human voice. The laughter 15 of one asleep, even if it be a little child,—the madman's laugh—the wild, screaming laugh of a born idiot,—are sounds that we sometimes tremble to hear, and would always willingly forget. Poets have imagined no utterance of fiends or hobgoblins so fearfully appropriate as 20 a laugh. And even the obtuse lime-burner felt his nerves shaken, as this strange man looked inward at his own heart, and burst into laughter that rolled away into the night, and was indistinctly reverberated among the hills.

"Joe," said he to his little son, "scamper down to 25 the tavern in the village, and tell the jolly fellows there that Ethan Brand has come back, and that he has found the Unpardonable Sin!"

The boy darted away on his errand, to which Ethan Brand made no objection, nor seemed hardly to notice it. 30 He sat on a log of wood looking steadfastly at the iron door of the kiln. When the child was out of sight, and his swift and light footsteps ceased to be heard treading first on the fallen leaves and then on the rocky mountain-path, the lime-burner began to regret his departure. He felt that the little fellow's presence had been a barrier between his guest and himself, and that he must now deal, heart to heart, with a man who, on his own confession, had committed the one only crime for which Heaven could afford no mercy. That crime, in its distinct blackness, seemed to overshadow him. The lime-burner's own sins rose up within him, and made his memory riotous with a throng of evil shapes that asserted their kindred with the Master Sin, whatever it might be, which it was within the scope of man's corrupted nature to conceive and cherish. They were all of one family; they went to and fro between his breast and Ethan Brand's, and carried dark greetings from one to the other.

Then Bartram remembered the stories which had grown traditionary in reference to this strange man, who had come upon him like a shadow of the night, and was making himself at home in his old place, after so long absence that the dead people, dead and buried for years, would have had more right to be at home, in any familiar spot, than he. Ethan Brand, it was said, had conversed with Satan himself in the lurid blaze of this very kiln. The legend had been matter of mirth heretofore, but looked grisly now. According to this tale, before Ethan Brand departed on his search, he had been accustomed to evoke a fiend from the hot furnace of the lime-kiln, night after night, in order to confer with him about the Unpardonable Sin; the man and the fiend each laboring to frame the image of some mode of guilt which could neither be atoned for nor forgiven. And, with the first gleam of light upon the mountain-top, the fiend crept in at the iron door, there to abide the intensest element of fire, until again summoned forth to share in the dreadful task of extending man's possible guilt beyond the scope of Heaven's else infinite mercy.

While the lime-burner was struggling with the horror of these thoughts, Ethan Brand rose from the log, and flung open the door of the kiln. The action was in such accordance with the idea in Bartram's mind, that he almost 5 expected to see the Evil One issue forth, red-hot from the raging furnace.

"Hold! hold!" cried he, with a tremulous attempt to laugh; for he was ashamed of his fears, although they overmastered him. "Don't, for mercy's sake, bring out 10 your devil now!"

"Man!" sternly replied Ethan Brand, "what need have I of the devil? I have left him behind me, on my track. It is with such half-way sinners as you that he busies himself. Fear not, because I open the door. I do 15 but act by old custom, and am going to trim your fire, like a lime-burner, as I was once."

He stirred the vast coals, thrust in more wood, and bent forward to gaze into the hollow prison-house of the fire, regardless of the fierce glow that reddened upon his 20 face. The lime-burner sat watching him, and half suspected his strange guest of a purpose, if not to evoke a fiend, at least to plunge bodily into the flames, and thus vanish from the sight of man. Ethan Brand, however, drew quietly back, and closed the door of the kiln.

25 "I have looked," said he, "into many a human heart that was seven times hotter with sinful passions than yonder furnace is with fire. But I found not there what I sought. No, not the Unpardonable Sin!"

"What is the Unpardonable Sin?" asked the lime-30 burner; and then he shrank further from his companion, trembling lest his question should be answered.

"It is a sin that grew within my own breast," replied Ethan Brand, standing erect, with a pride that distinguishes all enthusiasts of his stamp. "A sin that grew

nowhere else! The sin of an intellect that triumphed over the sense of brotherhood with man and reverence for God, and sacrificed everything to its own mighty claims! The only sin that deserves a recompense of immortal agony! Freely, were it to do again, would I incur the guilt. 5
Unshrinkingly I accept the retribution!"

"The man's head is turned," muttered the lime-burner to himself. "He may be a sinner, like the rest of us,—nothing more likely,—but, I'll be sworn, he is a madman, too." 10

Nevertheless he felt uncomfortable at his situation, alone with Ethan Brand on the wild mountain-side, and was right glad to hear the rough murmur of tongues, and the footsteps of what seemed a pretty numerous party, stumbling over the stones and rustling through the 15
underbrush. Soon appeared the whole lazy regiment that was wont to infest the village tavern, comprehending three or four individuals who had drunk flip beside the bar-room fire through all the winters, and smoked their pipes beneath the stoop through all the summers, since 20
Ethan Brand's departure. Laughing boisterously, and mingling all their voices together in unceremonious talk, they now burst into the moonshine and narrow streaks of firelight that illuminated the open space before the lime-kiln. Bartram set the door ajar again, flooding the 25
spot with light, that the whole company might get a fair view of Ethan Brand, and he of them.

There, among other old acquaintances, was a once ubiquitous man, now almost extinct, but whom we were formerly sure to encounter at the hotel of every thriving 30
village throughout the country. It was the stage-agent. The present specimen of the genus was a wilted and smoke-dried man, wrinkled and red-nosed, in a smartly-cut, brown, bob-tailed coat, with brass buttons, who, for

a length of time unknown, had kept his desk and corner in the bar-room, and was still puffing what seemed to be the same cigar that he had lighted twenty years before. He had great fame as a dry joker, though, perhaps, less 5 on account of any intrinsic humor than from a certain flavor of brandy-toddy and tobacco-smoke, which impregnated all his ideas and expressions, as well as his person. Another well-remembered though strangely-altered face was that of Lawyer Giles, as people still called him in 10 courtesy; an elderly ragamuffin, in his soiled shirt-sleeves and tow-cloth trousers. This poor fellow had been an attorney, in what he called his better days, a sharp practitioner, and in great vogue among the village litigants; but flip, and sling, and toddy, and cocktails, im-15 bibed at all hours, morning, noon, and night, had caused him to slide from intellectual to various kinds and degrees of bodily labor, till at last, to adopt his own phrase, he slid into a soap-vat. In other words, Giles was now a soap-boiler, in a small way. He had come to be but the 20 fragment of a human being, a part of one foot having been chopped off by an axe, and an entire hand torn away by the devilish grip of a steam-engine. Yet though the corporeal hand was gone, a spiritual member remained; for, stretching forth the stump, Giles steadfastly averred 25 that he felt an invisible thumb and fingers with as vivid a sensation as before the real ones were amputated. A maimed and miserable wretch he was; but one, nevertheless, whom the world could not trample on, and had no right to scorn, either in this or any previous stage of 30 his misfortunes, since he had still kept up the courage and spirit of a man, asked nothing in charity, and with his one hand—and that the left one—fought a stern battle against want and hostile circumstances.

Among the throng, too, came another personage, who,

with certain points of similarity to Lawyer Giles, had many more of difference. It was the village doctor; a man of some fifty years, whom, at an earlier period of his life, we introduced as paying a professional visit to Ethan Brand during the latter's supposed insanity. He 5 was now a purple-visaged, rude, and brutal, yet half-gentlemanly figure, with something wild, ruined, and desperate in his talk, and in all the details of his gesture and manners. Brandy possessed this man like an evil spirit, and made him as surly and savage as a wild beast, 10 and as miserable as a lost soul; but there was supposed to be in him such wonderful skill, such native gifts of healing, beyond any which medical science could impart, that society caught hold of him, and would not let him sink out of its reach. So, swaying to and fro upon his horse, 15 and grumbling thick accents at the bedside, he visited all the sick-chambers for miles about among the mountain towns, and sometimes raised a dying man, as it were, by miracle, or quite as often, no doubt, sent his patient to a grave that was dug many a year too soon. The doc- 20 tor had an everlasting pipe in his mouth, and as somebody said, in allusion to his habit of swearing, it was always alight with hell-fire.

These three worthies pressed forward, and greeted Ethan Brand each after his own fashion, earnestly invit- 25 ing him to partake of the contents of a certain black bottle, in which, as they averred, he would find something far better worth seeking for than the Unpardonable Sin. No mind, which has wrought itself by intense and solitary meditation into a high state of enthusiasm, can 30 endure the kind of contact with low and vulgar modes of thought and feeling to which Ethan Brand was now subjected. It made him doubt—and, strange to say, it was a painful doubt—whether he had indeed found the Unpardonable Sin, and found it within himself. The whole question on which he had exhausted life, and more than life, looked like a delusion.

"Leave me," he said bitterly, "ye brute beasts, that have made yourselves so, shriveling up your souls with fiery liquors! I have done with you. Years and years ago, I groped into your hearts, and found nothing there for my purpose. Get ye gone!"

"Why, you uncivil scoundrel," cried the fierce doctor, "is that the way you respond to the kindness of your best friends? Then let me tell you the truth. You have no more found the Unpardonable Sin than yonder boy Joe has. You are but a crazy fellow,—I told you so twenty years ago,—neither better nor worse than a crazy fellow, and the fit companion of old Humphrey, here!"

He pointed to an old man, shabbily dressed, with long white hair, thin visage, and unsteady eyes. For some years past this aged person had been wandering about among the hills, inquiring of all travelers whom he met for his daughter. The girl, it seemed, had gone off with a company of circus-performers; and occasionally tidings of her came to the village, and fine stories were told of her glittering appearance as she rode on horseback in the ring, or performed marvelous feats on the tight-rope.

The white-haired father now approached Ethan Brand, and gazed unsteadily into his face.

"They tell me you have been all over the earth," said he, wringing his hands with earnestness. "You must have seen my daughter, for she makes a grand figure in the world, and everybody goes to see her. Did she send any word to her old father, or say when she was coming back?"

Ethan Brand's eye quailed beneath the old man's.

That daughter, from whom he so earnestly desired a word of greeting, was the Esther of our tale, the very girl whom, with such cold and remorseless purpose, Ethan Brand had made the subject of a psychological experiment, and wasted, absorbed, and perhaps annihilated her 5 soul, in the process.

"Yes," murmured he, turning away from the hoary wanderer; "it is no delusion. There is an Unpardonable Sin!"

While these things were passing, a merry scene was 10 going forward in the area of cheerful light, beside the spring and before the door of the hut. A number of the youth of the village, young men and girls, had hurried up the hillside, impelled by curiosity to see Ethan Brand, the hero of so many a legend familiar to their childhood. 15 Finding nothing, however, very remarkable in his aspect,—nothing but a sun-burnt wayfarer, in plain garb and dusty shoes, who sat looking into the fire, as if he fancied pictures among the coals,—these young people speedily grew tired of observing him. As it happened, 20 there was other amusement at hand. An old German Jew, traveling with a diorama on his back, was passing down the mountain-road towards the village just as the party turned aside from it, and, in hopes of eking out the profits of the day, the showman had kept them company to the 25 lime-kiln.

"Come, old Dutchman," cried one of the young men, "let us see your pictures, if you can swear they are worth looking at!"

"O, yes, Captain," answered the Jew,—whether as a 30 matter of courtesy or craft, he styled everybody Captain,—"I shall show you, indeed, some very superb pictures!"

So, placing his box in a proper position, he invited the

young men and girls to look through the glass orifices of the machine, and proceeded to exhibit a series of the most outrageous scratchings and daubings, as specimens of the fine arts, that ever an itinerant showman had the face 5 to impose upon his circle of spectators. The pictures were worn out, moreover, tattered, full of cracks and wrinkles, dingy with tobacco-smoke, and otherwise in a most pitiable condition. Some purported to be cities, public edifices, and ruined castles in Europe; others represented Napoleon's 10 battles and Nelson's sea-fights; and in the midst of these would be seen a gigantic, brown, hairy hand,—which might have been mistaken for the Hand of Destiny, though, in truth, it was only the showman's,—pointing its forefinger to various scenes of the conflict, while its 15 owner gave historical illustrations. When, with much merriment at its abominable deficiency of merit, the exhibition was concluded, the German bade little Joe put his head into the box. Viewed through the magnifying glasses, the boy's round, rosy visage assumed the strangest 20 imaginable aspect of an immense Titanic child, the mouth grinning broadly, and the eyes and every other feature overflowing with fun at the joke. Suddenly, however, that merry face turned pale, and its expression changed to horror, for this easily impressed and excitable 25 child had become sensible that the eye of Ethan Brand was fixed upon him through the glass.

"You make the little man to be afraid, Captain," said the German Jew, turning up the dark and strong outline of his visage, from his stooping posture. "But 30 look again, and, by chance, I shall cause you to see somewhat that is very fine, upon my word!"

Ethan Brand gazed into the box for an instant, and then starting back, looked fixedly at the German. What had he seen? Nothing, apparently; for a curious youth, who had peeped in almost at the same moment, beheld only a vacant space of canvas.

"I remember you now," muttered Ethan Brand to the showman.

"Ah, Captain," whispered the Jew of Nuremburg, 5 with a dark smile, "I find it to be a heavy matter in my show-box,—this Unpardonable Sin! By my faith, Captain, it has wearied my shoulders this long day, to carry it over the mountain."

"Peace," answered Ethan Brand, sternly, "or get thee 10 into the furnace yonder!"

The Jew's exhibition had scarcely concluded, when a great, elderly dog,—who seemed to be his own master, as no person in the company laid claim to him,—saw fit to render himself the object of public notice. Hitherto, he 15 had shown himself a very quiet, well-disposed old dog, going round from one to another, and, by way of being sociable, offering his rough head to be patted by any kindly hand that would take so much trouble. But now, all of a sudden, this grave and venerable quadruped, 20 of his own mere motion, and without the slightest suggestion from anybody else, began to run round after his tail, which, to heighten the absurdity of the proceeding, was a great deal shorter than it should have been. Never was seen such headlong eagerness in pursuit of an object 25 that could not possibly be attained; never was heard such a tremendous outbreak of growling, snarling, barking, and snapping,—as if one end of the ridiculous brute's body were at deadly and most unforgivable enmity with the other. Faster and faster, round about went the cur; 30 and faster and still faster fled the unapproachable brevity of his tail; and louder and fiercer grew his yells of rage and animosity; until, utterly exhausted, and as far from the goal as ever, the foolish old dog ceased his performance as suddenly as he had begun it. The next moment he was as mild, quiet, sensible, and respectable in his deportment, as when he first scraped acquaintance with the company.

5 As may be supposed, the exhibition was greeted with universal laughter, clapping of hands, and shouts of encore, to which the canine performer responded by wagging all that there was to wag of his tail, but appeared totally unable to repeat his very successful effort to 10 amuse the spectators.

Meanwhile, Ethan Brand had resumed his seat upon the log, and moved, it might be, by a perception of some remote analogy between his own case and that of this self-pursuing cur, he broke into the awful laugh, which, 15 more than any other token, expressed the condition of his inward being. From that moment, the merriment of the party was at an end; they stood aghast, dreading lest the inauspicious sound should be reverberated around the horizon, and that mountain would thunder it to moun- 20 tain, and so the horror be prolonged upon their ears. Then, whispering one to another that it was late,—that the moon was almost down,—that the August night was growing chill,—they hurried homewards, leaving the lime-burner and little Joe to deal as they might with their 25 unwelcome guest. Save for these three human beings, the open space on the hillside was a solitude, set in a vast gloom of forest. Beyond that darksome verge, the fire-light glimmered on the stately trunks and almost black foliage of pines, intermixed with the lighter verdure of 30 sapling oaks, maples, and poplars, while here and there lay the gigantic corpses of dead trees, decaying on the leaf-strewn soil. And it seemed to little Joe—a timorous and imaginative child—that the silent forest was holding its breath, until some fearful thing should happen.

Starting from the log with a certain alacrity in his gait, and ascending the hillock of earth that was raised against the stone circumference of the lime-kiln, he thus reached the top of the structure. It was a space of perhaps ten feet across, from edge to edge, presenting a view of 5 the upper surface of the immense mass of broken marble with which the kiln was heaped. All these innumerable blocks and fragments of marble were red-hot and vividly on fire, sending up great spouts of blue flame, which quivered aloft and danced madly, as within a magic circle, 10 and sank and rose again, with continual and multitudinous activity. As the lonely man bent forward over this terrible body of fire, the blasting heat smote up against his person with a breath that, it might be supposed, would have scorched and shriveled him up in a moment. 15

Ethan Brand stood erect, and raised his arms on high. The blue flames played upon his face, and imparted the wild and ghastly light which alone could have suited its expression; it was that of a fiend on the verge of plunging into his gulf of intensest torment. 20

"O Mother Earth," cried he, "who art no more my Mother, and into whose bosom this frame shall never be resolved! O mankind, whose brotherhood I have cast off, and trampled thy great heart beneath my feet! O stars of heaven, that shone on me of old, as if to light 25 me onward and upward!—farewell all, and forever! Come, deadly element of Fire,—henceforth my familiar friend! Embrace me, as I do thee!"

That night the sound of a fearful peal of laughter rolled heavily through the sleep of the lime-burner and his 30 little son; dim shapes of horror and anguish haunted their dreams, and seemed still present in the rude hovel, when they opened their eyes to the daylight.

"Up, boy, up!" cried the lime-burner, staring about

him. "Thank Heaven, the night is gone, at last; and
rather than pass such another, I would watch my lime-
kiln, wide awake, for a twelvemonth. This Ethan Brand,
with his humbug of an Unpardonable Sin, has done me
5 no such mighty favor, in taking my place!"

He issued from the hut, followed by little Joe, who
kept fast hold of his father's hand. The early sunshine
was already pouring its gold upon the mountain-tops; and
though the valleys were still in shadow, they smiled
10 cheerfully in the promise of the bright day that was
hastening onward. The village, completely shut in by
hills, which swelled away gently about it, looked as if it
had rested peacefully in the hollow of the great hand of
Providence. Every dwelling was distinctly visible; the
15 little spires of the two churches pointed upwards, and
caught a fore-glimmering of brightness from the sun-gilt
skies upon their gilded weather-cocks. The tavern was
astir, and the figure of the old, smoke-dried stage-agent,
cigar in mouth, was seen beneath the stoop. Old Gray-
20 lock was glorified with a golden cloud upon his head.
Scattered likewise over the breasts of the surrounding
mountains, there were heaps of hoary mist, in fantastic
shapes, some of them far down into the valley, others
high up towards the summits, and still others, of the same
25 family of mist or cloud, hovering in the gold radiance
of the upper atmosphere. Stepping from one to another
of the clouds that rested on the hills, and thence to the
loftier brotherhood that sailed in air, it seemed almost
as if a mortal man might thus ascend into the heavenly
30 region. Earth was so mingled with sky that it was a
day-dream to look at it.

To supply that charm of the familiar and homely,
which Nature so readily adopts into a scene like this,
the stage-coach was rattling down the mountain-road, and

the driver sounded his horn, while echo caught up the notes, and intertwined them into a rich and varied and elaborate harmony, of which the original performer could lay claim to little share. The great hills played a concert among themselves, each contributing a strain of airy sweetness. 5

Little Joe's face brightened at once.

"Dear father," cried he, skipping cheerily to and fro, "that strange man is gone, and the sky and the mountains all seem glad of it." 10

"Yes," growled the lime-burner, with an oath, "but he has let the fire go down, and no thanks to him if five hundred bushels of lime are not spoiled. If I catch the fellow hereabouts again, I shall feel like tossing him into the furnace!" 15

With his long pole in his hand, he ascended to the top of the kiln. After a moment's pause, he called to his son.

"Come up here, Joe!" said he.

So little Joe ran up the hillock, and stood by his 20 father's side. The marble was all burnt into perfect, snow-white lime. But on its surface, in the midst of the circle,—snow-white too, and thoroughly converted into lime,—lay a human skeleton, in the attitude of a person who, after long toil, lies down to long repose. Within 25 the ribs—strange to say—was the shape of a human heart.

"Was the fellow's heart made of marble?" cried Bartram, in some perplexity at this phenomenon. "At any rate, it is burnt into what looks like special good lime; and taking all the bones together, my kiln is half 30 a bushel the richer for him."

So saying, the rude lime-burner lifted his pole, and, letting it fall upon the skeleton, the relics of Ethan Brand were crumbled into fragments.

RAB AND HIS FRIENDS *

By JOHN BROWN

FOUR-AND-THIRTY years ago, Bob Ainslie and I were coming up Infirmary Street from the Edinburgh High School our heads together, and our arms intertwisted, as only lovers and boys know how, or why.

5 When we got to the top of the street, and turned north, we espied a crowd at the Tron Church. "A dog-fight!" shouted Bob, and was off; and so was I, both of us all but praying that it might not be over before we got up! And is not this boy-nature? and human 10 nature too? and don't we all wish a house on fire not to be out before we see it? Dogs like fighting; old Isaac says they "delight" in it, and for the best of all reasons; and boys are not cruel because they like to see the fight. They see three of the great cardinal virtues of 15 dog or man—courage, endurance, and skill—in intense action. This is very different from a love of making dogs fight, and enjoying, and aggravating, and making gain by their pluck. A boy, be he ever so fond himself of fighting, if he be a good boy, hates and despises all this, but 20 he would have run off with Bob and me fast enough: it is a natural, and a not wicked interest, that all boys and men have in witnessing intense energy in action.

* DR. JOHN BROWN (1810-1882), author of this study of pathetic personality, was a Scottish physician. This story was included in a collection of sketches and papers entitled *Horæ Subsecivæ,* published in 1858. See also pp. 45-46.

Does any curious and finely ignorant woman wish to know how Bob's eye at a glance announced a dog-fight to his brain? He did not, he could not see the dogs fighting; it was a flash of an inference, a rapid induction. The crowd round a couple of dogs fighting is a crowd 5 masculine mainly, with an occasional active, compassionate woman, fluttering wildly round the outside, and using her tongue and her hands freely upon the men, as so many "brutes"; it is a crowd annular, compact, and mobile; a crowd centripetal, having its eyes and its heads 10 all bent downwards and inwards, to one common focus.

Well, Bob and I are up, and find it is not over: a small, thoroughbred, white bull-terrier is busy throttling a large shepherd's dog, unaccustomed to war, but not to be trifled with. They are hard at it; the scientific little 15 fellow doing his work in great style, his pastoral enemy fighting wildly, but with the sharpest of teeth and a great courage. Science and breeding, however, soon had their own; the Game Chicken, as the premature Bob called him, working his way up, took his final grip of poor 20 Yarrow's throat,—and he lay gasping and done for. His master, a brown, handsome, big young shepherd from Tweedsmuir, would have liked to have knocked down any man, would "drink up Esil, or eat a crocodile," for that part, if he had a chance: it was no use kicking the 25 little dog; that would only make him hold the closer. Many were the means shouted out in mouthfuls, of the best possible ways of ending it. "Water!" but there was none near, and many cried for it who might have got it from the well at Blackfriars Wynd. "Bite the tail!" 30 and a large, vague, benevolent middle-aged man, more desirous than wise, with some struggle got the bushy end of *Yarrow's* tail into his ample mouth, and bit it with all his might. This was more than enough for the much-enduring, much-perspiring shepherd, who, with a gleam of joy over his broad visage, delivered a terrific facer upon our large, vague, benevolent, middle-aged friend,—who went down like a shot.

5 Still the Chicken holds; death not far off. "Snuff! a pinch of snuff!" observed a calm, highly-dressed young buck, with an eye-glass in his eye. "Snuff, indeed!" growled the angry crowd, affronted and glaring. "Snuff! a pinch of snuff!" again observes the buck, but with 10 more urgency; whereon were produced several open boxes, and from a mull which may have been at Culloden, he took a pinch, knelt down, and presented it to the nose of the Chicken. The laws of physiology and of snuff take their course; the Chicken sneezes, and Yarrow is free!

15 The young pastoral giant stalks off with Yarrow in his arms,—comforting him.

But the Bull Terrier's blood is up, and his soul unsatisfied; he grips the first dog he meets, and discovering she is not a dog, in Homeric phrase, he makes a brief sort 20 of *amende,* and is off. The boys, with Bob and me at their head, are after him: down Niddry Street he goes, bent on mischief; up the Cowgate like an arrow,—Bob and I, and our small men, panting behind.

There under the single arch of the South Bridge, is a 25 huge mastiff, sauntering down the middle of the causeway, as if with his hands in his pockets: he is old, gray, brindled, as big as a little Highland bull, and has the Shakespearean dewlaps shaking as he goes.

The Chicken makes straight at him, and fastens on 30 his throat. To our astonishment, the great creature does nothing but stand still, hold himself up, and roar,—yes, roar; a long, serious, remonstrative roar. How is this? Bob and I are up to them. *He is muzzled!* The bailies had proclaimed a general muzzling, and his mas-

ter studying strength and economy mainly, had encompassed his huge jaws in a home-made apparatus, constructed out of the leather of some ancient *breechin*. His mouth was open as far it could; his lips curled up in rage,—a sort of terrible grin; his teeth gleaming, ready, 5
from out the darkness; the strap across his mouth tense as a bowstring; his whole frame stiff with indignation and surprise; his roar asking us all round, "Did you ever see the like of this?" He looked a statue of anger and astonishment, done in Aberdeen granite. 10

We soon had a crowd: the Chicken held on. "A knife!" cried Bob; and a cobbler gave him his knife: you know the kind of knife, worn away obliquely to a point and always keen. I put its edge to the tense leather; it ran before it; and then!—one sudden jerk of that enor- 15
mous head, a sort of dirty mist about his mouth, no noise,—and the bright and fierce little fellow is dropped, limp and dead. A solemn pause: this was more than any of us had bargained for. I turned the little fellow over, and saw he was quite dead; the mastiff had taken 20
him by the small of the back like a rat, and broken it.

He looked down at his victim appeased, ashamed, and amazed; snuffed him all over, stared at him, and taking a sudden thought, turned round and trotted off. Bob took the dead dog up, and said, "John, we'll bury him 25
after tea." "Yes," said I, and was off after the mastiff. He made up the Cowgate at a rapid swing; he had forgotten some engagement. He turned up the Candlemaker Row, and stopped at the Harrow Inn.

There was a carrier's cart ready to start, and a keen, 30
thin, impatient, black-a-vised little man, his hand at his gray horse's head, looking about angrily for something.

"Rab, ye thief!" said he, aiming a kick at my great friend, who drew cringing up, and avoiding the heavy shoe with more agility than dignity, and watching his master's eye, slunk dismayed under the cart,—his ears down, and as much as he had of tail down too.

What a man this must be,—thought I,—to whom my 5 tremendous hero turns tail! The carrier saw the muzzle hanging, cut and useless, from his neck, and I eagerly told him the story, which Bob and I always thought, and still think, Homer, or King David, or Sir Walter alone, were worthy to rehearse. The severe little man was 10 mitigated, and condescended to say, "Rab, my man, puir Rabbie,"—whereupon the stump of a tail rose up, the ears were cocked, the eyes filled, and were comforted; the two friends were reconciled. "Hupp!" and a stroke of the whip were given to Jess; and off went the three.

15 Bob and I buried the Game Chicken that night (we had not much of a tea) in the back-green of his house in Melville Street, No. 17, with considerable gravity and silence; and being at the time in the Iliad, and, like all boys, Trojans, we called him Hector, of course.

---

20 Six years have passed,—a long time for a boy and a dog; Bob Ainslie is off to the wars; I am a medical student, and clerk at Minto House Hospital. Rab I saw almost every week, on the Wednesday; and we had much pleasant intimacy. I found the way to his heart by fre- 25 quent scratching of his huge head, and an occasional bone. When I did not notice him he would plant himself straight before me, and stand wagging that bud of a tail, and looking up, with his head a little to the one side. His master I occasionally saw; he used to call me 30 "Maister John," but was laconic as any Spartan.

One fine October afternoon, I was leaving the hospital, when I saw the large gate open, and in walked Rab, with that great and easy saunter of his. He looked as if taking general possession of the place; like the Duke of Wellington entering a subdued city, satiated with vic- 5 tory and peace. After him came Jess, now white from age, with her cart; and in it a woman, carefully wrapped up,—the carrier leading the horse anxiously, and looking back. When he saw me, James (for his name was James Noble) made a curt and grotesque "boo," and 10 said, "Maister John, this is the mistress; she's got trouble in her breest,—some kind o' an income we're thinkin'."

By this time I saw the woman's face; she was sitting on a sack filled with straw, her husband's plaid round her, and his big-coat, with its large white metal buttons, 15 over her feet.

I never saw a more unforgettable face,—pale, serious, *lonely*,* delicate, sweet, without being at all what we call fine. She looked sixty, and had on a mutch, white as snow, with its black ribbon; her silvery, smooth hair 20 setting off her dark-gray eyes,—eyes such as one sees only twice or thrice in a lifetime, full of suffering, full also of the overcoming of it: her eyebrows black and delicate, and her mouth firm, patient, and contented, which few mouths ever are. 25

As I have said, I never saw a more beautiful countenance, or one more subdued to settled quiet. "Ailie," said James, "this is Maister John, the young doctor; Rab's freend, ye ken. We often speak aboot you, doctor." She smiled, and made a movement, but said nothing; and 30 prepared to come down, putting her plaid aside and rising. Had Solomon, in all his glory, been handing

* It is not easy giving this look by one word; it was expressive of her being so much of her life alone.

down the Queen of Sheba at his palace gate, he could not have done it more daintily, more tenderly, more like a gentleman, than did James the Howgate carrier, when he lifted down Ailie his wife. The contrast of his small,
5 swarthy, weather-beaten, keen, worldly face to hers—pale, subdued, and beautiful—was something wonderful. Rab looked on concerned and puzzled, but ready for anything that might turn up,—were it to strangle the nurse, the porter, or even me. Ailie and he seemed great friends.

10 "As I was sayin', she's got a kind o' trouble in her breest, doctor; wull ye tak' a look at it?" We walked into the consulting-room, all four; Rab grim and comic, willing to be happy and confidential if cause could be shown, willing also to be the reverse, on the same terms.
15 Ailie sat down, undid her open gown and her lawn handkerchief round her neck, and without a word showed me her right breast. I looked at and examined it carefully,—she and James watching me, and Rab eying all three. What could I say? there it was, that had once
20 been so soft, so shapely, so white, so gracious and bountiful, so "full of all blessed conditions,"—hard as a stone, a center of horrid pain, making that pale face, with its gray, lucid, reasonable eyes, and its sweet, resolved mouth, express the full measure of suffering overcome. Why was
25 that gentle, modest, sweet woman, clean and lovable, condemned by God to bear such a burden?

I got her away to bed. "May Rab and me bide?" said James. "*You* may; and Rab, if he will behave himself." "I'se warrant he's do that, doctor"; and in
30 slank the faithful beast. I wish you could have seen him. There are no such dogs now. He belonged to a lost tribe. As I have said, he was brindled and gray like Rubislaw granite; his hair short, hard, and close, like a lion's; his body thick-set, like a little bull,—a sort of com-

pressed Hercules of a dog. He must have been ninety pounds' weight, at the least; he had a large blunt head; his muzzle black as night, his mouth blacker than any night, a tooth or two—being all he had—gleaming out of his jaws of darkness. His head was scarred with the 5 records of old wounds, a sort of series of fields of battle all over it; one eye out, one ear cropped as close as was Archbishop Leighton's father's; the remaining eye had the power of two; and above it, and in constant communication with it, was a tattered rag of an ear, which 10 was forever unfurling itself, like an old flag; and then that bud of a tail, about one inch long, if it could in any sense be said to be long, being as broad as long,—the mobility, the instantaneousness of that bud were very funny and surprising, and its expressive twinklings and 15 winkings, the intercommunications between the eye, the ear, and it, were of the oddest and swiftest.

Rab had the dignity and simplicity of great size; and having fought his way all along the road to absolute supremacy, he was as mighty in his own line as Julius 20 Cæsar or the Duke of Wellington, and had the gravity * of all great fighters.

You must have often observed the likeness of certain men to certain animals, and of certain dogs to men. Now, I never looked at Rab without thinking of the 25 great Baptist preacher, Andrew Fuller.† The same large,

* A Highland game-keeper, when asked why a certain terrier, of singular pluck, was so much more solemn than the other dogs, said, "O, sir, life's full o' sairiousness to him,—he just never can get enuff o' fechtin'." 30

† Fuller was, in early life, when a farmer lad at Soham, famous as a boxer; not quarrelsome, but not without "the stern delight" a man of strength and courage feels in their exercise. Dr. Charles Stewart, of Dunearn, whose rare gifts and graces as a physician, a divine, a scholar, and a gentle- 35

heavy, menacing, combative, somber, honest countenance, the same deep inevitable eye, the same look,—as of thunder asleep, but ready,—neither a dog nor a man to be trifled with.

5 Next day, my master, the surgeon, examined Ailie. There was no doubt it must kill her, and soon. It could be removed—it might never return—it would give her speedy relief—she should have it done. She courtesied, looked at James, and said, "When?" "To-morrow," 10 said the kind surgeon,—a man of few words. She and James and Rab and I retired. I noticed that he and she spoke little, but seemed to anticipate everything in each other. The following day, at noon, the students came in, hurrying up the great stair. At the first landing-15 place, on a small, well-known blackboard, was a bit of paper fastened by wafers, and many remains of old wafers beside it. On the paper were the words,—"An operation to-day. J. B. *Clerk.*"

Up ran the youths, eager to secure good places: in they 20 crowded, full of interest and talk. "What's the case?" "Which side is it?"

Don't think them heartless; they are neither better nor worse than you or I; they get over their professional horrors, and into their proper work,—and in them pity, as 25 an *emotion,* ending in itself or at best in tears and a long-drawn breath, lessens, while pity as a *motive* is

man live only in the memory of those few who knew and survive him, liked to tell how Mr. Fuller used to say, that when he was in the pulpit, and saw a *buirdly* man come along the pas-30 sage, he would instinctively draw himself up, measure his imaginary antagonist, and forecast how he would deal with him, his hands meanwhile condensing into fists, and tending to "square." He must have been a hard hitter if he boxed as he preached,—what "The Fancy" would call "an ugly cus-35 tomer."

quickened, and gains power and purpose. It is well for poor human nature that it is so.

The operating theater is crowded; much talk and fun, and all the cordiality and stir of youth. The surgeon with his staff of assistants is there. In comes Ailie: 5 one look at her quiets and abates the eager students. That beautiful old woman is too much for them; they sit down, and are dumb, and gaze at her. These rough boys feel the power of her presence. She walks in quickly, but without haste; dressed in her mutch, her neckerchief, her 10 white dimity short-gown, her black bombazine petticoat, showing her white worsted stockings and her carpet-shoes. Behind her was James with Rab. James sat down in the distance, and took that huge and noble head between his knees. Rab looked perplexed and dan- 15 gerous; forever cocking his ear and dropping it as fast.

Ailie stepped up on a seat, and laid herself on the table, as her friend the surgeon told her; arranged herself, gave a rapid look at James, shut her eyes, rested herself on me, and took my hand. The operation was at once be- 20 gun; it was necessarily slow; and chloroform—one of God's best gifts to his suffering children—was then unknown. The surgeon did his work. The pale face showed its pain, but was still and silent. Rab's soul was working within him; he saw that something strange was go- 25 ing on,—blood flowing from his mistress, and she suffering; his ragged ear was up, and importunate; he growled, and gave now and then a sharp, impatient yelp; he would have liked to have done something to that man. But James had him firm, and gave him a *glower* from time 30 to time, and an intimation of a possible kick;—all the better for James, it kept his eye and his mind off Ailie.

It is over: she is dressed, steps gently and decently down from the table, looks for James; then turning to the surgeon and the students, she courtesies,—and in a low, clear voice, begs their pardon if she has behaved ill. The students—all of us—wept like children; the surgeon happed her up carefully,—and, resting on James and me, Ailie went to her room, Rab following. We put her to bed. James took off his heavy shoes, crammed with tackets, heel-capt and toe-capt, and put them carefully under the table saying, "Maister John, I'm for nane o' yer strynge nurse bodies for Ailie. I'll be her nurse, and I'll gang aboot on my stockin' soles as canny as pussy." And so he did; and handy and clever, and swift and tender as any woman, was that horny-handed, snell, peremptory little man. Everything she got he gave her: he seldom slept; and often I saw his small, shrewd eyes out of the darkness, fixed on her. As before, they spoke little.

Rab behaved well, never moving, showing us how meek and gentle he could be, and occasionally, in his sleep, letting us know that he was demolishing some adversary. He took a walk with me every day, generally to the Candlemaker Row; but he was somber and mild; declined doing battle, though some fit cases offered, and indeed submitted to sundry indignities; and was always very ready to turn, and came faster back, and trotted up the stair with much lightness, and went straight to that door.

Jess, the mare, had been sent, with her weather-worn car, to Howgate, and had doubtless her own dim and placid meditations and confusions, on the absence of her master and Rab, and her unnatural freedom from the road and her cart.

For some days Ailie did well. The wound healed "by the first intention"; for, as James said, "Oor Ailie's skin is ower clean to beil." The students came in quiet and anxious, and surrounded her bed. She said she liked to see their young, honest faces. The surgeon dressed her, and spoke to her in his own short, kind way, pitying her through his eyes, Rab and James outside the circle,—Rab being now reconciled, and even cordial, and having made up his mind that as yet nobody required worrying, but, as you may suppose, *semper paratus*.

So far well: but, four days after the operation, my patient had a sudden and long shivering, a "groosin'," as she called it. I saw her soon after; her eyes were too bright, her cheek colored; she was restless, and ashamed of being so; the balance was lost; mischief had begun. On looking at the wound, a blush of red told the secret: her pulse was rapid, her breathing anxious and quick, she wasn't herself, as she said, and was vexed at her restlessness. We tried what we could. James did everything, was everywhere; never in the way, never out of it; Rab subsided under the table into a dark place, and was motionless, all but his eye, which followed every one. Ailie got worse; began to wander in her mind, gently; was more demonstrative in her ways to James, rapid in her questions, and sharp at times. He was vexed, and said, "She was never that way afore; no, never." For a time she knew her head was wrong, and was always asking our pardon,—the dear, gentle old woman: then delirium set in strong, without pause. Her brain gave way, and then came that terrible spectacle,—

> "The intellectual power, through words and things,
> Went sounding on its dim and perilous way";

she sang bits of old songs and Psalms, stopping suddenly, mingling the Psalms of David and the diviner words of his Son and Lord with homely odds and ends and scraps of ballads.

Nothing more touching, or in a sense more strangely beautiful, did I ever witness. Her tremulous, rapid, affectionate, eager Scotch voice,—the swift, aimless, bewildered mind, the baffled utterance, the bright and perilous eye;
5 some wild words, some household cares, something for James, the names of the dead, Rab called rapidly and in a "fremyt" voice, and he starting up surprised, and slinking off as if he were to blame somehow, or had been dreaming he heard; many eager questions and beseech-
10 ings which James and I could make nothing of, and on which she seemed to set her all, and then sink back ununderstood. It was very sad, but better than many things that are not called sad. James hovered about, put out and miserable, but active and exact as ever; read
15 to her, when there was a lull, short bits from the Psalms, prose and meter, chanting the later in his own rude and serious way, showing great knowledge of the fit words, bearing up like a man, and doating over her as his "ain Ailie." "Ailie, ma woman!" "Ma ain bonnie
20 wee dawtie!"

The end was drawing on: the golden bowl was breaking; the silver cord was fast being loosed,—that *animula blandula, vagula, hospes, comesque,* was about to flee. The body and the soul—companions for sixty years—were
25 being sundered, and taking leave. She was walking alone through the valley of that shadow into which one day we must all enter—and yet she was not alone, for we know whose rod and staff were comforting her.

One night she had fallen quiet, and, as we hoped, asleep;
30 her eyes were shut. We put down the gas, and sat watching her. Suddenly she sat up in bed, and taking a bedgown which was lying on it rolled up, she held it eagerly to her breast,—to the right side. We could see her eyes bright with a surprising tenderness and joy, bending over

this bundle of clothes. She held it as a woman holds her sucking child; opening out her nightgown impatiently, and holding it close, and brooding over it, and murmuring foolish little words, as over one whom his mother comforteth, and who sucks and is satisfied. It was pitiful 5 and strange to see her wasted dying look, keen and yet vague,—her immense love.

"Preserve me!" groaned James, giving way. And then she rocked back and forward, as if to make it sleep, hushing it, and wasting on it her infinite fondness. 10 "Wae's me, doctor; I declare she's thinkin' it's that bairn." "What bairn?" "The only bairn we ever had; our wee Mysie, and she's in the Kingdom, forty years and mair." It was plainly true: the pain in the breast, telling its urgent story to a bewildered, ruined brain, 15 was misread and mistaken; it suggested to her the uneasiness of a breast full of milk, and then the child; and so again once more they were together, and she had her ain wee Mysie in her bosom.

This was the close. She sank rapidly: the delirium 20 left her; but, as she whispered, she was "clean silly"; it was the lightening before the final darkness. After having for some time lain still, her eyes shut, she said, "James!" He came close to her, and lifting up her calm, clear, beautiful eyes, she gave him a long look, 25 turned to me kindly but shortly, looked for Rab but could not see him, then turned to her husband again, as if she would never leave off looking, shut her eyes, and composed herself. She lay for some time breathing quick, and passed away so gently, that 30 when we thought she was gone, James, in his old-fashioned way, held the mirror to her face. After a long pause, one small spot of dimness was breathed out; it vanished away, and never returned, leaving the blank clear darkness of the mirror without a stain. "What is our life? it is even a vapor, which appeareth for a little time, and then vanisheth away."

Rab all this time had been full awake and motion-5 less; he came forward beside us; Ailie's hand, which James had held, was hanging down; it was soaked with his tears; Rab licked it all over carefully, looked at her, and returned to his place under the table.

James and I sat, I don't know how long, but for 10 some time,—saying nothing: he started up abruptly, and with some noise went to the table, and putting his right fore and middle fingers each into a shoe, pulled them out, and put them on, breaking one of the leather latchets, and muttering in anger, "I never did the like o' that 15 afore!"

I believe he never did; nor after either. "Rab!" he said roughly, and pointing with his thumb to the bottom of the bed. Rab leapt up, and settled himself; his head and eye to the dead face. "Maister John, ye'll wait 20 for me," said the carrier; and disappeared in the darkness, thundering downstairs in his heavy shoes. I ran to a front window; there he was, already round the house, and out at the gate, fleeing like a shadow.

I was afraid about him, and yet not afraid; so I sat 25 down beside Rab, and being wearied, fell asleep. I awoke from a sudden noise outside. It was November, and there had been a heavy fall of snow. Rab was *in statu quo;* he heard the noise too, and plainly knew it, but never moved. I looked out; and there, at the gate, in 30 the dim morning—for the sun was not up—was Jess and the cart,—a cloud of steam rising from the old mare. I did not see James; he was already at the door, and came up the stairs, and met me. It was less than three hours since he left, and he must have posted out—who knows how?—to Howgate, full nine miles off, yoked Jess, and driven her astonished into town. He had an armful of blankets, and was streaming with perspiration. He nodded to me, spread out on the floor two pairs of clean old blankets having at their corners, "A. G., 5 1794," in large letters in red worsted. These were the initials of Alison Græme, and James may have looked in at her from without,—himself unseen but not unthought of,—when he was "wat, wat, and weary," and after having walked many a mile over the hills, may 10 have seen her sitting, while "a' the lave were sleepin'"; and by the firelight working her name on the blankets, for her ain James's bed.

He motioned Rab down, and taking his wife in his arms, laid her in the blankets, and happed her carefully 15 and firmly up, leaving the face uncovered; and then lifting her, he nodded again sharply to me, and with a resolved but utterly miserable face strode along the passage, and downstairs, followed by Rab. I followed with a light; but he didn't need it. I went out, holding stupidly the 20 candle in my hand in the calm frosty air; we were soon at the gate. I could have helped him, but I saw he was not to be meddled with, and he was strong, and did not need it. He laid her down as tenderly, as safely, as he had lifted her out ten days before,—as tenderly as when 25 he had her first in his arms when she was only "A. G.,"—sorted her, leaving that beautiful sealed face open to the heavens; and then taking Jess by the head, he moved away. He did not notice me, neither did Rab, who presided behind the cart. I stood till they passed through 30 the long shadow of the College, and turned up Nicolson Street. I heard the solitary cart sound through the streets, and die away and come again; and I returned, thinking of that company going up Libberton Brae, then along Roslin Muir, the morning light touching the Pentlands and making them like on-looking ghosts; then down the hill through Auchindinny woods, past "haunted Woodhouselee"; and as daybreak came sweeping up the 5 bleak Lammermuirs, and fell on his own door, the company would stop, and James would take the key, and lift Ailie up again, laying her on her own bed, and, having put Jess up, would return with Rab and shut the door.

James buried his wife, with his neighbors mourning, 10 Rab inspecting the solemnity from a distance. It was snow, and that black ragged hole would look strange in the midst of the swelling spotless cushion of white. James looked after everything; then rather suddenly fell ill, and took to bed; was insensible when the doctor came, 15 and soon died. A sort of low fever was prevailing in the village, and his want of sleep, his exhaustion, and his misery made him apt to take it. The grave was not difficult to reopen. A fresh fall of snow had again made all things white and smooth; Rab once more looked on, 20 and slunk home to the stable.

And what of Rab? I asked for him next week at the new carrier who got the good-will of James's business, and was now master of Jess and her cart. "How's Rab?" He put me off, and said rather rudely, "What's 25 *your* business wi' the dowg?" I was not to be so put off. "Where's Rab?" He, getting confused and red, and intermeddling with his hair, said, "'Deed, sir, Rab's deid." "Dead! what did he die of?" "Weel, sir," said he, getting redder, "he didna exactly dee; he was killed. 30 I had to brain him wi' a rackpin; there was nae doin' wi' him. He lay in the treviss wi' the mear, and wadna come oot. I tempit him wi' kail and meat, but he wad tak naething, and keepit me frae feedin' the beast, and he was aye gur gurrin', and grup gruppin' me by the legs. I was laith to make awa wi' the auld dowg, his like wasna atween this and Thornhill,—but, 'deed, sir, I could do naething else." I believed him. Fit end for Rab, quick and complete. His teeth and his friends 5 gone, why should he keep the peace, and be civil?

THE SIRE DE MALÉTROIT'S DOOR *

By ROBERT LOUIS STEVENSON

DENIS DE BEAULIEU was not yet two-and-twenty, but he counted himself a grown man, and a very accomplished cavalier into the bargain. Lads were early formed in that rough, warfaring epoch; and when one has been 5 in a pitched battle and a dozen raids, has killed one's man in an honorable fashion, and knows a thing or two of strategy and mankind, a certain swagger in the gait is surely to be pardoned. He had put up his horse with due care, and supped with due deliberation; and then, 10 in a very agreeable frame of mind, went out to pay a visit in the gray of the evening. It was not a very wise proceeding on the young man's part. He would have done better to remain beside the fire or go decently to bed. For the town was full of the troops of Burgundy and 15 England under a mixed command; and though Denis was there on safe-conduct, his safe-conduct was like to serve him little on a chance encounter.

It was September, 1429; the weather had fallen sharp; a flighty piping wind, leaden with showers, beat 20 about the township; and the dead leaves ran riot along the streets. Here and there a window was already lighted up; and the noise of men-at-arms making merry over supper within, came forth in fits and was swal-

* ROBERT LOUIS STEVENSON (1850-1894), Scottish story-writer and essayist, published *The Sire de Malétroit's Door* in 1878. *Treasure Island* is his masterpiece in the long story. This story is used by the kind permission of Charles Scribner's Sons.

lowed up and carried away by the wind. The night fell swiftly; the flag of England, fluttering on the spire-top, grew ever fainter and fainter against the flying clouds—a black speck like a swallow in the tumultuous, leaden chaos of the sky. As the night fell the wind rose, and 5 began to hoot under archways and roar amid the tree-tops in the valley below the town.

Denis de Beaulieu walked fast and was soon knocking at his friend's door; but though he promised himself to stay only a little while and make an early return, 10 his welcome was so pleasant, and he found so much to delay him, that it was already long past midnight before he said good-by upon the threshold. The wind had fallen again in the meanwhile; the night was as black as the grave; not a star, nor a glimmer of moonshine, slipped 15 through the canopy of cloud. Denis was ill-acquainted with the intricate lanes of Chateau Landon; even by daylight he had found some trouble in picking his way; and in this absolute darkness he soon lost it altogether. He was certain of one thing only—to keep mounting the 20 hill; for his friend's house lay at the lower end, or tail, of Chateau Landon, while the inn was up at the head, under the great church spire. With this clue to go upon he stumbled and groped forward, now breathing more freely in open places where there was a good slice 25 of sky overhead, now feeling along the wall in stifling closes. It is an eerie and mysterious position to be thus submerged in opaque blackness in an almost unknown town. The silence is terrifying in its possibilities. The touch of cold window bars to the exploring hand startles 30 the man like the touch of a toad; the inequalities of the pavement shake his heart into his mouth; a piece of denser darkness threatens an ambuscade or a chasm in the pathway; and where the air is brighter, the houses put on strange and bewildering appearances, as if to lead him farther from his way. For Denis, who had to regain his inn without attracting notice, there was real danger as well as mere discomfort in the walk; and he went warily and boldly at once, and at every corner paused to make an observation.

He had been for some time threading a lane so narrow that he could touch a wall with either hand when it began to open out and go sharply downward. Plainly this lay no longer in the direction of his inn; but the hope of a little more light tempted him forward to reconnoiter. The lane ended in a terrace with a bartizan wall, which gave an outlook between high houses, as out of an embrasure, into the valley lying dark and formless several hundred feet below. Denis looked down, and could discern a few tree-tops waving and a single speck of brightness where the river ran across a weir. The weather was clearing up, and the sky had lightened, so as to show the outline of the heavier clouds and the dark margin of the hills. By the uncertain glimmer, the house on his left hand should be a place of some pretensions; it was surmounted by several pinnacles and turret-tops; the round stern of a chapel, with a fringe of flying buttresses, projected boldly from the main block; and the door was sheltered under a deep porch carved with figures and overhung by two long gargoyles. The windows of the chapel gleamed through their intricate tracery with a light as of many tapers, and threw out the buttresses and the peaked roof in a more intense blackness against the sky. It was plainly the hotel of some great family of the neighborhood; and as it reminded Denis of a town house of his own at Bourges, he stood for some time gazing up at it and mentally gauging the skill of the architects and the consideration of the two families.

There seemed to be no issue to the terrace but the lane by which he had reached it; he could only retrace his steps, but he had gained some notion of his whereabouts, and hoped by this means to hit the main thoroughfare and speedily regain the inn. He was reckoning without that chapter of accidents which was to make this night memorable above all others in his career; for he had not gone back above a hundred yards before he saw a light coming to meet him, and heard loud voices speaking together in the echoing narrows of the lane. It was a party of men-at-arms going the night round with torches. Denis assured himself that they had all been making free with the wine-bowl, and were in no mood to be particular about safe-conducts or the niceties of chivalrous war. It was as like as not that they would kill him like a dog and leave him where he fell. The situation was inspiriting but nervous. Their own torches would conceal him from sight, he reflected; and he hoped that they would drown the noise of his footsteps with their own empty voices. If he were but fleet and silent, he might evade their notice altogether.

Unfortunately, as he turned to beat a retreat, his foot rolled upon a pebble; he fell against the wall with an ejaculation, and his sword rang loudly on the stones. Two or three voices demanded who went there—some in French, some in English; but Denis made no reply, and ran the faster down the lane. Once upon the terrace, he paused to look back. They still kept calling after him, and just then began to double the pace in pursuit, with a considerable clank of armor, and great tossing of the torchlight to and fro in the narrow jaws of the passage.

Denis cast a look around and darted into the porch. There he might escape observation, or—if that were too much to expect—was in a capital posture whether for parley or defense. So thinking, he drew his sword and tried to set his back against the door. To his surprise, it yielded behind his weight; and though he turned in a 5 moment, continued to swing back on oiled and noiseless hinges, until it stood wide open on a black interior. When things fall out opportunely for the person concerned, he is not apt to be critical about the how or why, his own immediate personal convenience seeming a suffi- 10 cient reason for the strangest oddities and revolutions in our sublunary things; and so Denis, without a moment's hesitation, stepped within and partly closed the door behind him to conceal his place of refuge. Nothing was further from his thoughts than to close it altogether; 15 but for some inexplicable reason—perhaps by a spring or a weight—the ponderous mass of oak whipped itself out of his fingers and clanked to, with a formidable rumble and a noise like the falling of an automatic bar.

The round, at that very moment, debouched upon 20 the terrace and proceeded to summon him with shouts and curses. He heard them ferreting in the dark corners; the stock of a lance even rattled along the outer surface of the door behind which he stood; but these gentlemen were in too high a humor to be long delayed, and 25 soon made off down a corkscrew pathway which had escaped Denis's observation, and passed out of sight and hearing along the battlements of the town.

Denis breathed again. He gave them a few minutes' grace for fear of accidents, and then groped about for 30 some means of opening the door and slipping forth again. The inner surface was quite smooth, not a handle, not a molding, not a projection of any sort. He got his fingernails round the edges and pulled, but the mass was immovable. He shook it, it was as firm as a rock. Denis de Beaulieu frowned and gave vent to a little noiseless whistle. What ailed the door? he wondered. Why was it open? How came it to shut so easily and so effectually after him? There was something obscure and underhand about all this, that was little to the young man's 5 fancy. It looked like a snare; and yet who could suppose a snare in such a quiet by-street and in a house of so prosperous and even noble an exterior? And yet—snare or no snare, intentionally or unintentionally—here he was, prettily trapped; and for the life of him he could 10 see no way out of it again. The darkness began to weigh upon him. He gave ear; all was silent without, but within and close by he seemed to catch a faint sighing, a faint sobbing rustle, a little stealthy creak—as though many persons were at his side, holding themselves quite 15 still, and governing even their respiration with the extreme of slyness. The idea went to his vitals with a shock, and he faced about suddenly as if to defend his life. Then, for the first time, he became aware of a light about the level of his eyes and at some distance in the 20 interior of the house—a vertical thread of light, widening towards the bottom, such as might escape between two wings of arras over a doorway. To see anything was a relief to Denis; it was like a piece of solid ground to a man laboring in a morass; his mind seized upon it 25 with avidity; and he stood staring at it and trying to piece together some logical conception of his surroundings. Plainly there was a flight of steps ascending from his own level to that of this illuminated doorway; and indeed he thought he could make out another thread of 30 light, as fine as a needle and as faint as phosphorescence, which might very well be reflected along the polished wood of a handrail. Since he had begun to suspect that he was not alone, his heart had continued to beat with smothering violence, and an intolerable desire for action of any sort had possessed itself of his spirit. He was in deadly peril, he believed. What could be more natural than to mount the staircase, lift the curtain, and confront 5 his difficulty at once? At least he would be dealing with something tangible; at least he would be no longer in the dark. He stepped slowly forward with outstretched hands, until his foot struck the bottom step; then he rapidly scaled the stairs, stood for a moment to compose 10 his expression, lifted the arras, and went in.

He found himself in a large apartment of polished stone. There were three doors; one on each of three sides; all similarly curtained with tapestry. The fourth side was occupied by two large windows and a great stone 15 chimney-piece, carved with the arms of the Malétroits. Denis recognized the bearings, and was gratified to find himself in such good hands. The room was strongly illuminated; but it contained little furniture except a heavy table and a chair or two, the hearth was innocent 20 of fire, and the pavement was but sparsely strewn with rushes clearly many days old.

On a high chair beside the chimney, and directly facing Denis as he entered, sat a little old gentleman in a fur tippet. He sat with his legs crossed and his hands 25 folded, and a cup of spiced wine stood by his elbow on a bracket on the wall. His countenance had a strongly masculine cast; not properly human, but such as we see in the bull, the goat, or the domestic boar; something equivocal and wheedling, something greedy, brutal, and 30 dangerous. The upper lip was inordinately full, as though swollen by a blow or a toothache; and the smile, the peaked eyebrows, and the small, strong eyes were quaintly and almost comically evil in expression. Beautiful white hair hung straight all round his head, like a saint's, and fell in a single curl upon the tippet. His beard and mustache were the pink of venerable sweetness. Age, probably in consequence of inordinate precautions, had left no mark upon his hands; and the Malétroit hand was famous. It would be difficult to imagine anything 5 at once so fleshy and so delicate in design; the taper, sensual fingers were like those of one of Leonardo's women; the fork of the thumb made a dimpled protuberance when closed; the nails were perfectly shaped, and of a dead, surprising whiteness. It rendered his aspect tenfold more 10 redoubtable, that a man with hands like these should keep them devoutly folded like a virgin martyr—that a man with so intent and startling an expression of face should sit patiently on his seat and contemplate people with an unwinking stare, like a god, or a god's statue. His 15 quiescence seemed ironical and treacherous, it fitted so poorly with his looks.

Such was Alain, Sire de Malétroit.

Denis and he looked silently at each other for a second or two. 20

"Pray step in," said the Sire de Malétroit. "I have been expecting you all the evening."

He had not risen but he accompanied his words with a smile and a slight but courteous inclination of the head. Partly from the smile, partly from the strange musical 25 murmur with which the Sire prefaced his observation, Denis felt a strong shudder of disgust go through his marrow. And what with disgust and honest confusion of mind, he could scarcely get words together in reply.

"I fear," he said; "that this is a double accident. I am 30 not the person you suppose me. It seems you were looking for a visit; but for my part, nothing was further from my thoughts—nothing could be more contrary to my wishes—than this intrusion."

"Well, well," replied the old gentleman indulgently, "here you are, which is the main point. Seat yourself, my friend, and put yourself entirely at your ease. We shall arrange our little affairs presently."

5 Denis perceived that the matter was still complicated with some misconception, and he hastened to continue his explanations.

"Your door . . ." he began.

"About my door?" asked the other, raising his peaked 10 eyebrows. "A little piece of ingenuity." And he shrugged his shoulders. "A hospitable fancy! By your own account, you were not desirous of making my acquaintance. We old people look for such reluctance now and then; when it touches our honor, we cast about until 15 we find some way of overcoming it. You arrive uninvited, but believe me, very welcome."

"You persist in error, sir," said Denis. "There can be no question between you and me. I am a stranger in this countryside. My name is Denis, damoiseau 20 de Beaulieu. If you see me in your house, it is only——"

"My young friend," interrupted the other, "you will permit me to have my own ideas on that subject. They probably differ from yours at the present moment," he 25 added with a leer, "but time will show which of us is in the right."

Denis was convinced he had to do with a lunatic. He seated himself with a shrug, content to wait the upshot; and a pause ensued, during which he thought he could 30 distinguish a hurried gabbling as of prayer from behind the arras immediately opposite him. Sometimes there seemed to be but one person engaged, sometimes two; and the vehemence of the voice, low as it was, seemed to indicate either great haste or an agony of spirit. It occurred to him that this piece of tapestry covered the entrance to the chapel he had noticed from without.

The old gentleman meanwhile surveyed Denis from head to foot with a smile, and from time to time emitted little noises like a bird or a mouse, which seemed to indicate a high degree of satisfaction. This state of matters became rapidly insupportable; and Denis, to put an end to it, remarked politely that the wind had gone down.

The old gentleman fell into a fit of silent laughter, so prolonged and violent that he became quite red in the face. Denis got upon his feet at once, and put on his hat with a flourish.

"Sir," he said, "if you are in your wits, you have affronted me grossly. If you are out of them, I flatter myself I can find better employment for my brains than to talk with lunatics. My conscience is clear; you have made a fool of me from the first moment; you have refused to hear my explanations; and now there is no power under God will make me stay here any longer; and if I cannot make my way out in a more decent fashion, I will hack your door in pieces with my sword."

The Sire de Malétroit raised his right hand and wagged it at Denis with the fore and little fingers extended.

"My dear nephew," he said, "sit down."

"Nephew!" retorted Denis, "you lie in your throat;" and he snapped his fingers in his face.

"Sit down, you rogue!" cried the old gentleman, in a sudden, harsh voice, like the barking of a dog. "Do you fancy," he went on, "that when I had made my little contrivance for the door I had stopped short with that? If you prefer to be bound hand and foot till your bones ache, rise and try to go away. If you choose to remain a free young buck, agreeably conversing with an old gentleman—why, sit where you are in peace, and God be with you."

"Do you mean I am a prisoner?" demanded Denis.

5 "I state the facts," replied the other. "I would rather leave the conclusion to yourself."

Denis sat down again. Externally he managed to keep pretty calm; but within, he was now boiling with anger, now chilled with apprehension. He no longer 10 felt convinced that he was dealing with a madman. And if the old gentleman was sane, what, in God's name, had he to look for? What absurd or tragical adventure had befallen him? What countenance was he to assume?

While he was thus unpleasantly reflecting, the arras 15 that overhung the chapel door was raised, and a tall priest in his robes came forth and, giving a long, keen stare at Denis, said something in an undertone to Sire de Malétroit.

"She is in a better frame of spirit?" asked the latter.

20 "She is more resigned, messire," replied the priest.

"Now the Lord help her, she is hard to please!" sneered the old gentleman. "A likely stripling—not ill-born—and of her own choosing, too? Why, what more would the jade have?"

25 "The situation is not usual for a young damsel," said the other, "and somewhat trying to her blushes."

"She should have thought of that before she began the dance! It was none of my choosing, God knows that: but since she is in it, by our lady, she shall carry it to the 30 end." And then addressing Denis, "Monsieur de Beaulieu," he asked, "may I present you to my niece? She has been waiting your arrival, I may say, with even greater impatience than myself."

Denis had resigned himself with a good grace—all he

desired was to know the worst of it as speedily as possible; so he rose at once, and bowed in acquiescence. The Sire de Malétroit followed his example and limped, with the assistance of the chaplain's arm, towards the chapel-door. The priest pulled aside the arras, and all three entered. The building had considerable architectural pretensions. A light groining sprang from six stout columns, and hung down in two rich pendants from the center of the vault. The place terminated behind the altar in a round end, embossed and honeycombed with a superfluity of ornament in relief, and pierced by many little windows shaped like stars, trefoils, or wheels. These windows were imperfectly glazed, so that the night air circulated freely in the chapel. The tapers, of which there must have been half a hundred burning on the altar, were unmercifully blown about; and the light went through many different phases of brilliancy and semi-eclipse. On the steps in front of the altar knelt a young girl richly attired as a bride. A chill settled over Denis as he observed her costume; he fought with desperate energy against the conclusion that was being thrust upon his mind; it could not—it should not—be as he feared.

"Blanche," said the Sire, in his most flute-like tones, "I have brought a friend to see you, my little girl; turn round and give him your pretty hand. It is good to be devout; but it is necessary to be polite, my niece."

The girl rose to her feet and turned toward the newcomers. She moved all of a piece; and shame and exhaustion were expressed in every line of her fresh young body; and she held her head down and kept her eyes upon the pavement, as she came slowly forward. In the course of her advance, her eyes fell upon Denis de Beaulieu's feet—feet of which he was justly vain, be it remarked, and wore in the most elegant accouterment even while traveling. She paused—started, as if his yellow boots had conveyed some shocking meaning—and glanced suddenly up into the wearer's countenance. Their eyes met; 5 shame gave place to horror and terror in her looks; the blood left her lips; with a piercing scream she covered her face with her hands and sank upon the chapel floor.

"That is not the man!" she cried. "My uncle, that is not the man!"

10 The Sire de Malétroit chirped agreeably. "Of course not," he said, "I expected as much. It was so unfortunate you could not remember his name."

"Indeed," she cried, "indeed, I have never seen this person till this moment—I have never so much as set 15 eyes upon him—I never wish to see him again. Sir," she said, turning to Denis, "if you are a gentleman, you will bear me out. Have I ever seen you—have you ever seen me—before this accursed hour?"

"To speak for myself, I have never had that pleasure," 20 answered the young man. "This is the first time, messire, that I have met with your engaging niece."

The old gentleman shrugged his shoulders.

"I am distressed to hear it," he said. "But it is never too late to begin. I had little more acquaintance with 25 my own late lady ere I married her; which proves," he added, with a grimace, "that these impromptu marriages may often produce an excellent understanding in the long run. As the bridegroom is to have a voice in the matter, I will give him two hours to make up for lost time be- 30 fore we proceed with the ceremony." And he turned toward the door, followed by the clergyman.

The girl was on her feet in a moment. "My uncle, you cannot be in earnest," she said. "I declare before God I will stab myself rather than be forced on that young man. The heart rises at it; God forbids such marriages; you dishonor your white hair. Oh, my uncle, pity me! There is not a woman in all the world but would prefer death to such a nuptial. Is it possible," she added, faltering—" is it possible that you do not believe me—that you still think this "—and she pointed at Denis with a tremor of anger and contempt—" that you still think *this* to be the man?"

"Frankly," said the old gentleman, pausing on the threshold, "I do. But let me explain to you once for all, Blanche de Malétroit, my way of thinking about this affair. When you took it into your head to dishonor my family and the name that I have borne, in peace and war, for more than three-score years, you forfeited, not only the right to question my designs, but that of looking me in the face. If your father had been alive, he would have spat on you and turned you out of doors. His was the hand of iron. You may bless your God you have only to deal with the hand of velvet, mademoiselle. It was my duty to get you married without delay. Out of pure good-will, I have tried to find your own gallant for you. And I believe I have succeeded. But before God and all the holy angels, Blanche de Malétroit, if I have not, I care not one jack-straw. So let me recommend you to be polite to our young friend; for upon my word, your next groom may be less appetizing."

And with that he went out, with the chaplain at his heels; and the arras fell behind the pair.

The girl turned upon Denis with flashing eyes.

"And what, sir," she demanded, "may be the meaning of all this?"

"God knows," returned Denis, gloomily. "I am a prisoner in this house, which seems full of mad people. More I know not; and nothing do I understand."

"And pray how came you here?" she asked.

He told her as briefly as he could. "For the rest," he added, "perhaps you will follow my example, and tell me the answer to all these riddles, and what, in God's
5 name, is like to be the end of it."

She stood silent for a little, and he could see her lips tremble and her tearless eyes burn with a feverish luster. Then she pressed her forehead in both hands.

"Alas, how my head aches!" she said wearily—"to
10 say nothing of my poor heart! But it is due to you to know my story, unmaidenly as it must seem. I am called Blanche de Malétroit; I have been without father or mother for—oh! for as long as I can recollect, and indeed I have been most unhappy all my life. Three months
15 ago a young captain began to stand near me every day in church. I could see that I pleased him; I am much to blame, but I was so glad that anyone should love me; and when he passed me a letter, I took it home with me and read it with great pleasure. Since that time he has
20 written many. He was so anxious to speak with me, poor fellow! and kept asking me to leave the door open some evening that we might have two words upon the stair. For he knew how much my uncle trusted me." She gave something like a sob at that, and it was a moment before
25 she could go on. "My uncle is a hard man, but he is very shrewd," she said at last. "He has performed many feats in war, and was a great person at court, and much trusted by Queen Isabeau in old days. How he came to suspect me I cannot tell; but it is hard to keep any-
30 thing from his knowledge; and this morning, as we came from mass, he took my hand into his, forced it open, and read my little billet, walking by my side all the while. When he finished, he gave it back to me with great politeness. It contained another request to have the door

left open; and this has been the ruin of us all. My uncle kept me strictly in my room until evening, and then ordered me to dress myself as you see me—a hard mockery for a young girl, do you not think so? I suppose, when he could not prevail with me to tell him the young captain's name, he must have laid a trap for him: into which, alas! you have fallen in the anger of God. I looked for much confusion; for how could I tell whether he was willing to take me for his wife on these sharp terms? He might have been trifling with me from the first; or I might have made myself too cheap in his eyes. But truly I had not looked for such a shameful punishment as this! I could not think that God would let a girl be so disgraced before a young man. And now I tell you all; and I can scarcely hope that you will not despise me."

Denis made her a respectful inclination.

"Madam," he said, "you have honored me by your confidence. It remains for me to prove that I am not unworthy of the honor. Is Messire de Malétroit at hand?"

"I believe he is writing in the salle without," she answered.

"May I lead you thither, madam?" asked Denis, offering his hand with his most courtly bearing.

She accepted it; and the pair passed out of the chapel, Blanche in a very drooping and shamefast condition, but Denis strutting and ruffling in the consciousness of a mission, and the boyish certainty of accomplishing it with honor.

The Sire de Malétroit rose to meet them with an ironical obeisance.

"Sir," said Denis, with the grandest possible air, "I believe I am to have some say in the matter of this marriage; and let me tell you at once, I will be no party to

forcing the inclination of this young lady. Had it been freely offered to me, I should have been proud to accept her hand, for I perceive she is as good as she is beautiful; but as things are, I have now the honor, messire, of
5 refusing."

Blanche looked at him with gratitude in her eyes; but the old gentleman only smiled and smiled, until his smile grew positively sickening to Denis.

"I am afraid," he said, "Monsieur de Beaulieu, that
10 you do not perfectly understand the choice I have offered you. Follow me, I beseech you, to this window." And he led the way to one of the large windows which stood open on the night. "You observe," he went on, "there is an iron ring in the upper masonry, and reeved through
15 that, a very efficacious rope. Now, mark my words: if you should find your disinclination to my niece's person insurmountable, I shall have you hanged out of this window before sunrise. I shall only proceed to such an extremity with the greatest regret, you may believe me.
20 For it is not at all your death that I desire, but my niece's establishment in life. At the same time, it must come to that if you prove obstinate. Your family, Monsieur de Beaulieu, is very well in its way; but if you sprang from Charlemagne, you should not refuse the hand
25 of a Malétroit with impunity—not if she had been as common as the Paris road—not if she were as hideous as the gargoyle over my door. Neither my niece nor you, nor my own private feelings, move me at all in this matter. The honor of my house has been compromised;
30 I believe you to be the guilty person, at least you are now in the secret; and you can hardly wonder if I request you to wipe out the stain. If you will not, your blood be on your own head! It will be no great satisfaction to me to have your interesting relics kicking their heels in the

breeze below my windows, but half a loaf is better than no bread, and if I cannot cure the dishonor, I shall at least stop the scandal."

There was a pause.

"I believe there are other ways of settling such imbroglios among gentlemen," said Denis. "You wear a sword, and I hear you have used it with distinction."

The Sire de Malétroit made a signal to the chaplain, who crossed the room with long silent strides and raised the arras over the third of the three doors. It was only a moment before he let it fall again; but Denis had time to see a dusky passage full of armed men.

"When I was a little younger, I should have been delighted to honor you, Monsieur de Beaulieu," said Sire Alain; "but I am now too old. Faithful retainers are the sinews of age, and I must employ the strength I have. This is one of the hardest things to swallow as a man grows up in years; but with a little patience, even this becomes habitual. You and the lady seem to prefer the salle for what remains of your two hours; and as I have no desire to cross your preference, I shall resign it to your use with all the pleasure in the world. No haste!" he added, holding up his hand, as he saw a dangerous look come into Denis de Beaulieu's face. "If your mind revolt against hanging, it will be time enough two hours hence to throw yourself out of the window or upon the pikes of my retainers. Two hours of life are always two hours. A great many things may turn up in even as little a while as that. And, besides, if I understand her appearance, my niece has something to say to you. You will not disfigure your last hours by a want of politeness to a lady?"

Denis looked at Blanche, and she made him an imploring gesture.

It is likely that the old gentleman was hugely pleased at this symptom of an understanding; for he smiled on both, and added sweetly: "If you will give me your word of honor, Monsieur de Beaulieu, to await my return at 5 the end of the two hours before attempting anything desperate, I shall withdraw my retainers, and let you speak in greater privacy with mademoiselle."

Denis again glanced at the girl, who seemed to beseech him to agree.

10 "I give you my word of honor," he said.

Messire de Malétroit bowed, and proceeded to limp about the apartment, clearing his throat the while with that odd musical chirp which had already grown so irritating in the ears of Denis de Beaulieu. He first pos-15 sessed himself of some papers which lay upon the table; then he went to the mouth of the passage and appeared to give an order to the men behind the arras; and lastly he hobbled out through the door by which Denis had come in, turning upon the threshold to address a last 20 smiling bow to the young couple, and followed by the chaplain with a hand-lamp.

No sooner were they alone than Blanche advanced towards Denis with her hands extended. Her face was flushed and excited, and her eyes shone with tears.

25 "You shall not die!" she cried, "you shall marry me after all."

"You seem to think, madam," replied Denis, "that I stand much in fear of death."

"Oh, no, no," she said, "I see you are no poltroon. 30 It is for my own sake—I could not bear to have you slain for such a scruple."

"I am afraid," returned Denis, "that you underrate the difficulty, madam. What you may be too generous to refuse, I may be too proud to accept. In a moment of noble feeling towards me, you forgot what you perhaps owe to others."

He had the decency to keep his eyes on the floor as he said this, and after he had finished, so as not to spy upon her confusion. She stood silent for a moment, then walked suddenly away, and falling on her uncle's chair, fairly burst out sobbing. Denis was in the acme of embarrassment. He looked round, as if to seek for inspiration, and seeing a stool, plumped down upon it for something to do. There he sat, playing with the guard of his rapier, and wishing himself dead a thousand times over, and buried in the nastiest kitchen-heap in France. His eyes wandered round the apartment, but found nothing to arrest them. There were such wide spaces between furniture, the light fell so badly and cheerlessly over all, the dark outside air looked in so coldly through the windows, that he thought he had never seen a church so vast, nor a tomb so melancholy. The regular sobs of Blanche de Malétroit measured out the time like the ticking of a clock. He read the device upon the shield over and over again, until his eyes became obscured; he stared into shadowy corners until he imagined they were swarming with horrible animals; and every now and again he awoke with a start, to remember that his last two hours were running, and death was on the march.

Oftener and oftener, as the time went on, did his glance settle on the girl herself. Her face was bowed forward and covered with her hands, and she was shaken at intervals by the convulsive hiccough of grief. Even thus she was not an unpleasant object to dwell upon, so plump and yet so fine, with a warm brown skin, and the most beautiful hair, Denis thought, in the whole world of womankind. Her hands were like her uncle's; but they were more in place at the end of her young arms, and looked infinitely soft and caressing. He remembered how her blue eyes had shone upon him, full of anger, pity, and innocence. And the more he dwelt on her perfections, the uglier death looked, and the more deeply was 5 he smitten with penitence at her continued tears. Now he felt that no man could have the courage to leave a world which contained so beautiful a creature; and now he would have given forty minutes of his last hour to have unsaid his cruel speech.

10 Suddenly a hoarse and ragged peal of cockcrow rose to their ears from the dark valley below the windows. And this shattering noise in the silence of all around was like a light in a dark place, and shook them both out of their reflections.

15 "Alas, can I do nothing to help you?" she said, looking up.

"Madam," replied Denis, with a fine irrelevancy, "if I have said anything to wound you, believe me, it was for your own sake and not for mine."

20 She thanked him with a tearful look.

"I feel your position cruelly," he went on. "The world has been bitter hard on you. Your uncle is a disgrace to mankind. Believe me, madam, there is no young gentleman in all France but would be glad of my oppor-25 tunity, to die in doing you a momentary service."

"I know already that you can be very brave and generous," she answered. "What I *want* to know is whether I can serve you—now or afterwards," she added, with a quaver.

30 "Most certainly," he answered with a smile. "Let me sit beside you as if I were a friend, instead of a foolish intruder; try to forget how awkwardly we are placed to one another; make my last moments go pleasantly; and you will do me the chief service possible."

"You are very gallant," she added, with a yet deeper sadness . . . "very gallant . . . and it somehow pains me. But draw nearer, if you please; and if you find anything to say to me, you will at least make certain of a very friendly listener. Ah! Monsieur de Beaulieu," she broke forth—"ah! Monsieur de Beaulieu, how can I look you in the face?" And she fell to weeping again with a renewed effusion.

"Madam," said Denis, taking her hand in both of his, "reflect on the little time I have before me, and the great bitterness into which I am cast by the sight of your distress. Spare me, in my last moments, the spectacle of what I cannot cure even with the sacrifice of my life."

"I am very selfish," answered Blanche. "I will be braver, Monsieur de Beaulieu, for your sake. But think if I can do you no kindness in the future—if you have no friends to whom I could carry your adieux. Charge me as heavily as you can; every burden will lighten, by so little, the invaluable gratitude I owe you. Put it in my power to do something more for you than weep."

"My mother is married again, and has a young family to care for. My brother Guichard will inherit my fiefs; and if I am not in error, that will content him amply for my death. Life is a little vapor that passeth away, as we are told by those in holy orders. When a man is in a fair way and sees all life open in front of him, he seems to himself to make a very important figure in the world. His horse whinnies to him; the trumpets blow and the girls look out of window as he rides into town before his company; he receives many assurances of trust and regard—sometimes by express in a letter—sometimes face to face, with persons of great consequence falling on his neck. It is not wonderful if his head is turned for a time. But once he is dead, were he as brave as Hercules or as wise as Solomon, he is soon forgotten. It is not ten years since my father fell, with many other knights around him, in a very fierce encounter, and I do not think that any one of them, nor so much as 5 the name of the fight, is now remembered. No, no, madam, the nearer you come to it, you see that death is a dark and dusty corner, where a man gets into his tomb and has the door shut after him till the judgment day. I have few friends just now, and once I am dead I shall have 10 none."

"Ah, Monsieur de Beaulieu!" she exclaimed, "you forget Blanche de Malétroit."

"You have a sweet nature, madam, and you are pleased to estimate a little service far beyond its worth."

15 "It is not that," she answered. "You mistake me if you think I am easily touched by my own concerns. I say so, because you are the noblest man I have ever met; because I recognize in you a spirit that would have made even a common person famous in the land."

20 "And yet here I die in a mousetrap—with no more noise about it than my own squeaking," answered he.

A look of pain crossed her face, and she was silent for a little while. Then a light came into her eyes, and with a smile she spoke again.

25 "I cannot have my champion think meanly of himself. Anyone who gives his life for another will be met in Paradise by all the heralds and angels of the Lord God. And you have no such cause to hang your head. For . . . Pray, do you think me beautiful?" she asked, with a 30 deep flush.

"Indeed, madam, I do," he said.

"I am glad of that," she answered heartily. "Do you think there are many men in France who have been asked in marriage by a beautiful maiden—with her own lips—and who have refused her to her face? I know you men would half despise such a triumph; but believe me, we women know more of what is precious in love. There is nothing that should set a person higher in his own esteem; and we women would prize nothing more dearly." 5

"You are very good," he said; "but you cannot make me forget that I was asked in pity and not for love."

"I am not so sure of that," she replied, holding down her head. "Hear me to an end, Monsieur de Beaulieu. I know how you must despise me; I feel you are right 10 to do so; I am too poor a creature to occupy one thought of your mind, although, alas! you must die for me this morning. But when I asked you to marry me, indeed, and indeed, it was because I respected and admired you, and loved you with my whole soul, from the very moment 15 that you took my part against my uncle. If you had seen yourself, and how noble you looked, you would pity rather than despise me. And now," she went on, hurriedly checking him with her hand, "although I have laid aside all reserve and told you so much, remember 20 that I know your sentiments towards me already. I would not, believe me, being nobly born, weary you with importunities into consent. I too have a pride of my own: and I declare before the holy mother of God, if you should now go back from your word already given, I 25 would no more marry you than I would marry my uncle's groom."

Denis smiled a little bitterly.

"It is a small love," he said, "that shies at a little pride." 30

She made no answer, although she probably had her own thoughts.

"Come hither to the window," he said with a sigh. "Here is the dawn."

And indeed the dawn was already beginning. The hollow of the sky was full of essential daylight, colorless and clean; and the valley underneath was flooded with a gray reflection. A few thin vapors clung in the coves of the forest or lay along the winding course of the river. The scene disengaged a surprising effect of stillness, which was hardly interrupted when the cocks began once more to crow among the steadings. Perhaps the same fellow who had made so horrid a clangor in the darkness not half an hour before, now sent up the merriest cheer to greet the coming day. A little wind went bustling and eddying among the tree-tops underneath the windows. And still the daylight kept flooding insensibly out of the east, which was soon to grow incandescent and cast up that red-hot cannon-ball, the rising sun.

Denis looked out over all this with a bit of a shiver. He had taken her hand, and retained it in his almost unconsciously.

"Has the day begun already?" she said; and then, illogically enough: "the night has been so long! Alas! what shall we say to my uncle when he returns?"

"What you will," said Denis, and he pressed her fingers in his.

She was silent.

"Blanche," he said, with a swift, uncertain, passionate utterance, "you have seen whether I fear death. You must know well enough that I would as gladly leap out of that window into the empty air as to lay a finger on you without your free and full consent. But if you care for me at all do not let me lose my life in a misapprehension; for I love you better than the whole world; and though I will die for you blithely, it would be like all the joys of Paradise to live on and spend my life in your service."

As he stopped speaking, a bell began to ring loudly in the interior of the house; and a clatter of armor in the corridor showed that the retainers were returning to their 5 post, and the two hours were at an end.

"After all that you have heard?" she whispered, leaning towards him with her lips and eyes.

"I have heard nothing," he replied.

"The captain's name was Florimond de Champdivers," 10 she said in his ear.

"I did not hear it," he answered, taking her supple body in his arms, and covered her wet face with kisses.

A melodious chirping was audible behind, followed by a beautiful chuckle, and the voice of Messire de Malé- 15 troit wished his new nephew a good-morning.

ON GREENHOW HILL *

By RUDYARD KIPLING

"OHÉ, *Ahmed din! Shafiz Ullah ahoo!* Bahadur Khan, where are you? Come out of the tents, as I have done, and fight against the English. Don't kill your own kin! Come out to me!"

5 The deserter from a native corps was crawling round the outskirts of the camp, firing at intervals, and shouting invitations to his old comrades. Misled by the rain and the darkness, he came to the English wing of the camp, and with his yelping and rifle practice disturbed the 10 men. They had been making roads all day, and were tired.

Ortheris was sleeping at Learoyd's feet. "Wot's all that?" he said, thickly. Learoyd snored, and a Snider bullet ripped its way through the tent wall. The men 15 swore. "It's that bloomin' deserter from the Aurangabadis," said Ortheris. "Git up, some one, an' tell 'im 'e's come to the wrong shop."

"Go to sleep, little man," said Mulvaney, who was steaming nearest the door. "I can't rise an' expaytiate 20 with him. 'Tis rainin' intrenchin' tools outside."

"'Tain't because you bloomin' can't. It's 'cause you

* RUDYARD KIPLING (1865—), an Anglo-Indian, first made his reputation by Indian stories, and by local-color narratives, of which this tale is an example. He is now a resident of England. This story was first published in *Macmillan's Magazine*, September, 1890. See also pp. 67-74, 76.

bloomin' won't, ye long, limp, lousy, lazy beggar you. 'Ark to 'im 'owling!"

"Wot's the good of argyfying? Put a bullet into the swine! 'E's keepin' us awake!" said another voice.

A subaltern shouted angrily, and a dripping sentry 5 whined from the darkness—

"'Tain't no good, sir. I can't see 'im. 'E's 'idin' somewhere down 'ill."

Ortheris tumbled out of his blanket. "Shall I try to get 'im, sir?" said he. 10

"No," was the answer; "lie down. I won't have the whole camp shooting all round the clock. Tell him to go and pot his friends."

Ortheris considered for a moment. Then, putting his head under the tent wall, he called, as a 'bus conductor 15 calls in a block, "'Igher up, there! 'Igher up!"

The men laughed, and the laughter was carried down wind to the deserter, who, hearing that he had made a mistake, went off to worry his own regiment half a mile away. He was received with shots, for the Aurang- 20 abadis were very angry with him for disgracing their colors.

"An' that's all right," said Ortheris, withdrawing his head as he heard the hiccough of the Sniders in the dis- tance. "S'elp me Gawd, tho', that man's not fit to 25 live—messin' with my beauty-sleep this way."

"Go out and shoot him in the morning, then," said the subaltern, incautiously. "Silence in the tents now! Get your rest, men!"

Ortheris lay down with a happy little sigh, and in 30 two minutes there was no sound except the rain on the canvas and the all-embracing and elemental snoring of Learoyd.

The camp lay on a bare ridge of the Himalayas, and

for a week had been waiting for a flying column to make connection. The nightly rounds of the deserter and his friends had become a nuisance.

In the morning the men dried themselves in hot sun-
5 shine and cleaned their grimy accouterments. The native regiment was to take its turn of road-making that day while the Old Regiment loafed.

"I'm goin' to lay fer a shot at that man," said Ortheris, when he had finished washing out his rifle. "'E comes
10 up the water-course every evenin' about five o'clock. If we go and lie out on the north 'ill a bit this afternoon we'll get 'im."

"You're a bloodthirsty little mosquito," said Mulvaney, blowing blue clouds into the air. "But I suppose
15 I will have to come wid you. Fwhere's Jock?"

"Gone out with the Mixed Pickles, 'cause 'e thinks 'isself a bloomin' marksman," said Ortheris, with scorn.

The "Mixed Pickles" were a detachment of picked shots, generally employed in clearing spurs of hills when
20 the enemy were too impertinent. This taught the young officers how to handle men, and did not do the enemy much harm. Mulvaney and Ortheris strolled out of camp, and passed the Aurangabadis going to their road-making.

"You've got to sweat to-day," said Ortheris, genially.
25 "We're going to get your man. You didn't knock 'im out last night by any chance, any of you?"

"No. The pig went away mocking us. I had one shot at him," said a private. "He's my cousin, and *I* ought to have cleared our dishonor. But good luck to
30 you."

They went cautiously to the north hill, Ortheris leading, because, as he explained, "this is a long-range show, an' I've got to do it." His was an almost passionate devotion to his rifle, which, by barrack-room report, he was supposed to kiss every night before turning in. Charges and scuffles he held in contempt, and, when they were inevitable, slipped between Mulvaney and Learoyd, bidding them to fight for his skin as well as their own. They never failed him. He trotted along, questing like a hound on a broken trail, through the wood of the north hill. At last he was satisfied, and threw himself down on the soft pine-needle slope that commanded a clear view of the water-course and a brown bare hillside beyond it. The trees made a scented darkness in which an army corps could have hidden from the sun-glare without.

" 'Ere's the tail o' the wood," said Ortheris. " 'E's got to come up the water-course, 'cause it gives 'im cover. We'll lay 'ere. 'Tain't not 'arf so bloomin' dusty neither."

He buried his nose in a clump of scentless white violets. No one had come to tell the flowers that the season of their strength was long past, and they had bloomed merrily in the twilight of the pines.

" This is something like," he said, luxuriously. " Wot a 'evinly clear drop for a bullet acrost. How much d' you make it, Mulvaney? "

" Seven hunder. Maybe a trifle less, bekase the air's so thin."

Wop! wop! wop! went a volley of musketry on the rear face of the north hill.

" Curse them Mixed Pickles firin' at nothin'! They'll scare 'arf the country."

" Thry a sightin' shot in the middle of the row," said Mulvaney, the man of many wiles. " There's a red rock yonder he'll be sure to pass. Quick! "

Ortheris ran his sight up to six hundred yards and fired. The bullet threw up a feather of dust by a clump of gentians at the base of the rock.

"Good enough!" said Ortheris, snapping the scale down. "You snick your sights to mine, or a little lower. You're always firin' high. But remember, first shot to me. Oh, Lordy! but it's a lovely afternoon."

5 The noise of the firing grew louder, and there was a tramping of men in the wood. The two lay very quiet, for they knew that the British soldier is desperately prone to fire at anything that moves or calls. Then Learoyd appeared, his tunic ripped across the breast by a bullet, 10 looking ashamed of himself. He flung down on the pine-needles, breathing in snorts.

"One o' them damned gardeners o' th' Pickles," said he, fingering the rent. "Firin' to th' right flank, when he knowed I was there. If I knew who he was I'd 'a' ripped 15 the hide off 'un. Look at ma tunic!"

"That's the spishil trustability av a marksman. Train him to hit a fly wid a stiddy rest at seven hunder, an' he'll loose on anythin' he sees or hears up to th' mile. You're well out av that fancy-firin' gang, Jock. Stay 20 here."

"Bin firin' at the bloomin' wind in the bloomin' tree-tops," said Ortheris, with a chuckle. "I'll show you some firin' later on."

They wallowed in the pine-needles, and the sun 25 warmed them where they lay. The Mixed Pickles ceased firing and returned to camp, and left the wood to a few scared apes. The water-course lifted up its voice in the silence and talked foolishly to the rocks. Now and again the dull thump of a blasting charge three miles away told 30 that the Aurangabadis were in difficulties with their road-making. The men smiled as they listened, and lay still soaking in the warm leisure. Presently Learoyd, between the whiffs of his pipe:

"Seems queer—about 'im yonder—desertin' at all."

" 'E'll be a bloomin' side queerer when I've done with 'im," said Ortheris. They were talking in whispers, for the stillness of the wood and the desire of slaughter lay heavy upon them.

" I make no doubt he had his reasons for desertin'; but, my faith! I make less doubt ivry man has good reason for killin' him," said Mulvaney.

" Happen there was a lass tewed up wi' it. Men do more than that for th' sake of a lass."

" They make most av of us 'list. They've no manner av right to make us desert."

" Ah, they make us 'list, or their fathers do," said Learoyd, softly, his helmet over his eyes.

Ortheris' brows contracted savagely. He was watching the valley. " If it's a girl, I'll shoot the beggar twice over, an' second time for bein' a fool. You're blasted sentimental all of a sudden. Thinkin' o' your last near shave?"

" Nay, lad; ah was but thinkin' o' what had happened."

" An' fwhat has happened, ye lumberin' child av calamity, that you're lowing like a cow-calf at the back av the pasture, an' suggestin' invidious excuses for the man Stanley's goin' to kill. Ye'll have to wait another hour yet, little man. Spit it out, Jock, an' bellow melojus to the moon. It takes an earthquake or a bullet graze to fetch aught out av you. Discourse, Don Juan! The a-moors of Lotharius Learoyd. Stanley, kape a rowlin' rig'mental eye on the valley."

" It's along o' yon hill there," said Learoyd, watching the bare sub-Himalayan spur that reminded him of his Yorkshire moors. He was speaking more to himself than his fellows. " Ay," said he; " Rumbolds Moor stands up ower Skipton town, an' Greenhow Hill stands

up ower Pately Brigg. I reckon you've never heard tell o' Greenhow Hill, but yon bit o' bare stuff, if there was nobbut a white road windin', is like it, strangely like. Moors an' moors—moors wi' never a tree for shelter, an'
5 gray houses wi' flag-stone rooves, and pewits cryin', an' a windhover goin' to and fro just like these kites. And cold! A wind that cuts you like a knife. You could tell Greenhow Hill folk by the red-apple color o' their cheeks an' nose tips, an' their blue eyes, driven into pin-points
10 by the wind. Miners mostly, burrowin' for lead i' th' hillsides, followin' the trail of th' ore vein same as a field-rat. It was the roughest minin' I ever seen. Yo'd come on a bit o' creakin' wood windlass like a well-head, an' you was let down i' th' bight of a rope, fendin'
15 yoursen off the side wi' one hand, carryin' a candle stuck in a lump o' clay with t'other, an' clickin' hold of a rope with t'other hand."

"An' that's three of them," said Mulvaney. "Must be a good climate in those parts."

20 Learoyd took no heed.

"An' then yo' came to a level, where you crept on your hands an' knees through a mile o' windin' drift, an' you come out into a cave-place as big as Leeds Town-hall, with an engine pumpin' water from workin's 'at went
25 deeper still. It's a queer country, let alone minin', for the hill is full of those natural caves, an' the rivers an' the becks drops into what they call pot-holes, an' come out again miles away."

"Wot was you doin' there?" said Ortheris.

30 "I was a young chap then, an' mostly went wi' 'osses, leadin' coal and lead ore; but at th' time I'm tellin' on I was drivin' the wagon team i' the big sumph. I didn't belong to that countryside by rights. I went there be-cause of a little difference at home, an' at fust I took

up wi' a rough lot. One night we'd been drinkin', and I must ha' hed more than I could stand, or happen th' ale was none so good. Though i' them days, by for God, I never seed bad ale." He flung his arms over his head and gripped a vast handful of white violets. "Nah," said he, "I never seed the ale I could not drink, the 'bacca I could not smoke, nor the lass I could not kiss. Well, we mun have a race home, the lot on us. I lost all th' others, an' when I was climbin' ower one of them walls built o' loose stones, I comes down into the ditch, stones an' all, an' broke my arm. Not as I knowed much about it, for I fell on th' back o' my head, an' was knocked stupid like. An' when I come to mysen it were mornin', an' I were lyin' on the settle i' Jesse Roantree's house-place, an' 'Liza Roantree was settin' sewin'. I ached all ower, and my mouth were like a lime-kiln. She gave me a drink out of a china mug wi' gold letters—'A Present from Leeds,'—as I looked at many and many a time after. 'Yo're to lie still while Doctor Warbottom comes, because your arm's broken, an' father has sent a lad to fetch him. He found yo' when he was goin' to work, an' carried you here on his back,' sez she. 'Oa!' sez I; an' I shet my eyes, for I felt ashamed o' mysen. 'Father's gone to his work these three hours, an' he said he'd tell 'em to get somebody to drive the tram.' The clock ticked an' a bee comed in the house, an' they rung i' my head like mill-wheels. An' she give me another drink an' settled the pillow. 'Eh, but yo're young to be getten drunk an' such like, but yo' won't do it again, will yo'?' 'Noa,' sez I. 'I wouldn't if she'd not but stop they mill-wheels clatterin'.'"

"Faith, it's a good thing to be nursed by a woman when you're sick!" said Mulvaney. "Dirt cheap at the price av twenty broken heads."

Ortheris turned to frown across the valley. He had not been nursed by many women in his life.

"An' then Doctor Warbottom comes ridin' up, an' Jesse Roantree along with 'im. He was a high-larned
5 doctor, but he talked wi' poor folks same as theirsens. 'What's tha bin agaate on naa?' he sings out. 'Brekkin tha thick head?' An' he felt me all over. 'That's none broken. Tha' nobbut knocked a bit sillier than ordinary, an' that's daaft eneaf.' An' soa he went on, callin'
10 me all the names he could think on, but settin' my arm, wi' Jesse's help, as careful as could be. 'Yo' mun let the big oaf bide here a bit, Jesse,' he says, when he had strapped me up an' given me a dose o' physic; 'an' you an' 'Liza will tend him, though he's scarcelins worth the
15 trouble. An' tha'll lose tha work,' sez he, 'an' tha'll be upon th' Sick Club for a couple o' months an' more. Doesn't tha think tha's a fool?'"

"But whin was a young man, high or low, the other av a fool, I'd like to know?" said Mulvaney.
20 "Sure, folly's the only safe way to wisdom, for I've thried it."

"Wisdom!" grinned Ortheris, scanning his comrades with uplifted chin. "You're bloomin' Solomons, you two, ain't you?"

25 Learoyd went calmly on, with a steady eye like an ox chewing the cud. "And that was how I comed to know 'Liza Roantree. There's some tunes as she used to sing—aw, she were always singin'—that fetches Greenhow Hill before my eyes as fair as yon brow across there. And she
30 would learn me to sing bass, an' I was to go to th' chapel wi' 'em, where Jesse and she led the singin', th' old man playin' the fiddle. He was a strange chap, old Jesse, fair mad wi' music, an' he made me promise to learn the big fiddle when my arm was better. It belonged to him, and

it stood up in a big case alongside o' th' eight-day clock, but Willie Satterthwaite, as played it in the chapel, had getten deaf as a door-post, and it vexed Jesse, as he had to rap him ower his head wi' th' fiddle-stick to make him give ower sawin' at th' right time. 5

"But there was a black drop in it all, an' it was a man in a black coat that brought it. When th' Primitive Methodist preacher came to Greenhow, he would always stop wi' Jesse Roantree, an' he laid hold of me from th' beginning. It seemed I wor a soul to be saved, an' he 10 meaned to do it. At th' same time I jealoused 'at he were keen o' savin' 'Liza Roantree's soul as well, an' I could ha' killed him many a time. An' this went on till one day I broke out, an' borrowed th' brass for a drink from 'Liza. After fower days I come back, wi' my tail between my 15 legs, just to see 'Liza again. But Jesse were at home, an' th' preacher—th' Reverend Amos Barraclough. 'Liza said naught, but a bit o' red come into her face as were white of a regular thing. Says Jesse, tryin' his best to be civil: 'Nay, lad, it's like this. You've getten to 20 choose which way it's goin' to be. I'll ha' nobody across ma doorsteps as goes a-drinkin', an' borrows my lass's money to spend i' their drink. Ho'd tha tongue, 'Liza,' sez he when she wanted to put in a word 'at I were welcome to th' brass, an' she were none afraid that I wouldn't 25 pay it back. Then the reverend cuts in, seein' as Jesse were losin' his temper, an' they fair beat me among them. But it were 'Liza, as looked an' said naught, as did more than either o' their tongues, an' soa I concluded to get converted." 30

"Fwhat!" shouted Mulvaney. Then, checking himself, he said, softly: "Let be! Let be! Sure the Blessed Virgin is the mother of all religion an' most women; an' there's a dale av piety in a girl if the men would only let it stay there. I'd ha' been converted myself under the circumstances."

"Nay, but," pursued Learoyd, with a blush, "I meaned it."

5 Ortheris laughed as loudly as he dared, having regard to his business at the time.

"Ay, Ortheris, you may laugh, but you didn't know yon preacher Barraclough—a little white-faced chap wi' a voice as 'u'd wile a bird off an a bush, and a way o' layin' 10 hold of folks as made them think they'd never had a live man for a friend before. You never saw him, an'—an'—you never seed 'Liza Roantree—never seed 'Liza Roantree. . . . Happen it was as much 'Liza as th' preacher and her father, but anyways they all meaned it, 15 an' I was fair shamed o' mysen, an' so become what they called a changed character. And when I think on, it's hard to believe as yon chap going to prayer-meetin's, chapel, and class-meetin's were me. But I never had naught to say for mysen, though there was a deal o' 20 shoutin', and old Sammy Strother, as were almost clemmed to death and doubled up with the rheumatics, would sing out, 'Joyful! joyful!' and 'at it were better to go up to heaven in a coal-basket than down to hell i' a coach an' six. And he would put his poor old claw on my shoulder, 25 sayin': 'Doesn't tha feel it, tha great lump? Doesn't tha feel it?' An' sometimes I thought I did, and then again I thought I didn't, an' how was that?"

"The iverlastin' nature av mankind," said Mulvaney. "An', furthermore, I misdoubt you were built for the 30 Primitive Methodians. They're a new corps anyways. I hold by the Ould Church, for she's the mother of them all—ay, an' the father, too. I like her bekase she's most remarkable regimental in her fittings. I may die in Honolulu, Nova Zambra, or Cape Cayenne, but wherever I die, me bein' fwhat I am, an' a priest handy, I go under the same orders an' the same words an' the same unction as tho' the pope himself come down from the dome av St. Peter's to see me off. There's neither high nor low, nor broad nor deep, not betwixt nor be- 5 tween with her, an' that's what I like. But mark you, she's no manner av Church for a wake man, bekase she takes the body and the soul av him, onless he has his proper work to do. I remember when my father died, that was three months comin' to his grave; begad 10 he'd ha' sold the sheebeen above our heads for ten minutes' quittance of purgathory. An' he did all he could. That's why I say it takes a strong man to deal with the Ould Church, an' for that reason you'll find so many women go there. An' that same's a conundrum." 15

"Wot's the use o' worritin' 'bout these things?" said Ortheris. "You're bound to find all out quicker nor you want to, any'ow." He jerked the cartridge out of the breech-block into the palm of his hand. "'Ere's my chaplain," he said, and made the venomous black-headed bullet 20 bow like a marionette. "'E's goin' to teach a man all about which is which, an' wot's true, after all, before sundown. But wot 'appened after that, Jock?"

"There was one thing they boggled at, and almost shut th' gate i' my face for, and that were my dog Blast, 25 th' only one saved out o' a litter o' pups as was blowed up when a keg o' minin' powder loosed off in th' storekeeper's hut. They liked his name no better than his business, which was fightin' every dog he comed across; a rare good dog, wi' spots o' black and pink on his face, 30 one ear gone, and lame o' one side wi' being driven in a basket through an iron roof, a matter of half a mile.

"They said I mun give him up 'cause he were

worldly and low; and would I let mysen be shut out of heaven for the sake of a dog? 'Nay,' says I, 'if th' door isn't wide enough for th' pair on us, we'll stop outside, for we'll none be parted.' And th' preacher spoke up for Blast, as had a likin' for him from th' first—I reckon that was why I come to like th' preacher—and wouldn't hear o' changin' his name to Bless, as some o' them wanted. So th' pair on us became reg'lar chapel members. But it's hard for a young chap o' my build to cut traces from the world, th' flesh, an' the devil all av a heap. Yet I stuck to it for a long time, while th' lads as used to stand about th' town-end an' lean ower th' bridge, spittin' into th' beck o' a Sunday, would call after me, 'Sitha, Learoyd, when's tha bean to preach, 'cause we're comin' to hear tha.' 'Ho'd tha jaw! He hasn't getten th' white choaker on ta morn,' another lad would say, and I had to double my fists hard i' th' bottom of my Sunday coat, and say to mysen, 'If 'twere Monday and I warn't a member o' the Primitive Methodists, I'd leather all th' lot of yond'.' That was th' hardest of all—to know that I could fight and I mustn't fight."

Sympathetic grunts from Mulvaney.

"So what wi' singin', practicin', and class-meetin's, and th' big fiddle, as he made me take between my knees, I spent a deal o' time i' Jesse Roantree's house-place. But often as I was there, th' preacher fared to me to go oftener, and both th' old an' th' young woman were pleased to have him. He lived i' Pately Brigg, as were a goodish step off, but he come. He come all the same. I liked him as well or better as any man I'd ever seen i' one way, and yet I hated him wi' all my heart i' t'other, and we watched each other like cat and mouse, but civil as you please, for I was on my best behavior, and he was that fair and open that I was bound to be fair with him. Rare and good company he was, if I hadn't wanted to wring his cliver little neck half of the time. Often and often when he was goin' from Jesse's I'd set him a bit on the road."

"See 'im 'ome, you mean?" said Ortheris. 5

"Aye. It's a way we have i' Yorkshire o' seein' friends off. Yon was a friend as I didn't want to come back, and he didn't want me to come back neither, and so we'd walk together toward Pately, and then he'd set me back again, and there we'd be twal two o'clock i' 10 the mornin' settin' each other to an fro like a blasted pair o' pendulums twixt hill and valley, long after th' light had gone out i' 'Liza's window, as both on us had been looking at, pretending to watch the moon."

"Ah!" broke in Mulvaney, "ye'd no chanst against 15 the maraudin' psalm-singer. They'll take the airs an' the graces, instid av the man, nine times out av ten, an' they only find the blunder later—the wimmen."

"That's just where yo're wrong," said Learoyd, reddening under the freckled tan of his cheek. "I was th' 20 first wi' 'Liza, an' yo'd think that were enough. But th' parson were a steady-gaited sort o' chap, and Jesse were strong o' his side, and all th' women i' the congregation dinned it to 'Liza 'at she were fair fond to take up wi' a wastrel ne'er-do-weel like me, as was scarcelins 25 respectable, and a fighting-dog at his heels. It was all very well for her to be doing me good and saving my soul, but she must mind as she didn't do herself harm. They talk o' rich folk bein' stuck up an' genteel, but for cast-iron pride o' respectability, there's naught like poor 30 chapel folk. It's as cold as th' wind o' Greenhow Hill—aye, and colder, for 'twill never change. And now I come to think on it, one of the strangest things I know is 'at they couldn't abide th' thought o' soldiering. There's a vast o' fightin' i' th' Bible, and there's a deal of Methodists i' th' army; but to hear chapel folk talk yo'd think that soldierin' were next door, an' t'other side, to hangin'. I' their meetin's all their talk is o' fightin'. When 5 Sammy Strother were struck for sommat to say in his prayers, he'd sing out: 'The sword o' th' Lord and o' Gideon.' They were allus at it about puttin' on th' whole armor o' righteousness, an' fightin' the good fight o' faith. And then, atop o' 't all, they held a prayer- 10 meetin' ower a young chap as wanted to 'list, and nearly deafened him, till he picked up his hat and fair ran away. And they'd tell tales in th' Sunday-school o' bad lads as had been thumped and brayed for bird-nesting o' Sundays and playin' truant o' week-days, and how they took 15 to wrestlin', dog-fightin', rabbit-runnin', and drinkin', till at last, as if 'twere a hepitaph on a gravestone, they damned him across th' moors wi', 'an' then he went and 'listed for a soldier,' an' they'd all fetch a deep breath, and throw up their eyes like a hen drinkin'."

20 "Fwhy is it?" said Mulvaney, bringing down his hands on his thigh with a crack. "In the name av God, fwhy is it? I've seen it, tu. They cheat an' they swindle, an' they lie an' they slander, an' fifty things fifty times worse; but the last an' the worst, by their reckonin', is to 25 serve the Widdy honest. It's like the talk av childer—seein' things all round."

"Plucky lot of fightin' good fights of whatsername they'd do if we didn't see they had a quiet place to fight in. And such fightin' as theirs is! Cats on the tiles. 30 T'other callin' to which to come on. I'd give a month's pay to get some o' them broad-backed beggars in London sweatin' through a day's road-makin' an' a night's rain. They'd carry on a deal afterward—same as we're supposed to carry on. I've bin turned out of a measly 'arf license pub. down Lambeth way, full o' greasy kebmen, 'fore now," said Ortheris with an oath.

"Maybe you were dhrunk," said Mulvaney, soothingly.

"Worse nor that. The Forders were drunk. I was wearin' the queen's uniform." 5

"I'd not particular thought to be a soldier i' them days," said Learoyd, still keeping his eye on the bare hill opposite, "but this sort o' talk put it i' my head. They was so good, th' chapel folk, that they tumbled ower t'other side. But I stuck to it for 'Liza's sake, specially as she was learning me to sing the bass part in a horotorio as Jesse were getting up. She sung like a throstle hersen, and we had practicin's night after night for a matter of three months." 10 15

"I know what a horotorio is," said Ortheris, pertly. "It's a sort of chaplain's singsong—words all out of the Bible, and hullabaloojah choruses."

"Most Greenhow Hill folks played some instrument or t'other, an' they all sung so you might have heard them miles away, and they was so pleased wi' the noise they made they didn't fair to want anybody to listen. The preacher sung high seconds when he wasn't playin' the flute, an' they set me, as hadn't got far with the big fiddle, again' Willie Satterthwaite, to jog his elbow when he had to get a' gate playin'. Old Jesse was happy if ever a man was, for he were th' conductor an' th' first fiddle an' th' leadin' singer, beatin' time wi' his fiddle-stick, till at times he'd rap with it on the table, and cry out: 'Now, you mun all stop; it's my turn.' And he'd face round to his front, fair sweatin' wi' pride, to sing the tenor solos. But he were grandest i' th' chorus, waggin' his head, flinging his arms round like a windmill, and singin' hisself black in the face. A rare singer were Jesse. 20 25 30

"Yo' see, I was not o' much account wi' 'em all exceptin' to Eliza Roantree, and I had a deal o' time settin' quiet at meeting and horotorio practices to hearken their talk, and if it were strange to me at beginnin', it got stranger still at after, when I was shut on it, and could study what it meaned.

"Just after th' horotorios come off, 'Liza, as had allus been weakly like, was took very bad. I walked Doctor Warbottom's horse up and down a deal of times while he were inside, where they wouldn't let me go, though I fair ached to see her.

"'She'll be better i' noo, lad—better i' noo,' he used to say. 'Tha mun ha' patience.' Then they said if I was quiet I might go in, and th' Reverend Amos Barraclough used to read to her lyin' propped up among th' pillows. Then she began to mend a bit, and they let me carry her on th' settle, and when it got warm again she went about same as afore. Th' preacher and me and Blast was a deal together i' them days, and i' one way we was rare good comrades. But I could ha' stretched him time and again with a good-will. I mind one day he said he would like to go down into th' bowels o' th' earth, and see how th' Lord had builded th' framework o' the everlastin' hills. He was one of them chaps as had a gift o' sayin' things. They rolled off the tip of his clever tongue, same as Mulvaney here, as would ha' made a rale good preacher if he had nobbut given his mind to it. I lent him a suit o' miner's kit as almost buried th' little man, and his white face, down i' th' coat collar and hat flap, looked like the face of a boggart, and he cowered down i' th' bottom o' the wagon. I was drivin' a tram as led up a bit of an incline up to th' cave where the engine was pumpin', and where th' ore was brought up and put into th' wagons as went down o' themselves, me puttin' th' brake on and th' horses a-trottin' after. Long as it was daylight we were good friends, but when we got fair into th' dark, and could nobbut see th' day shinin' at the hole like a lamp at a street end, I feeled downright wicked. My religion dropped all away from me when I looked back at him as were always comin' between me and Eliza. The talk was 'at they were to be wed when she got better, an' I couldn't get her to say yes or nay to it. He began to sing a hymn in his thin voice, and I came out wi' a chorus that was all cussin' an' swearin' at my horses, an' I began to know how I hated him. He were such a little chap, too. I could drop him wi' one hand down Garstang's copperhole—a place where th' beck slithered ower th' edge on a rock, and fell wi' a bit of a whisper into a pit as no rope i' Greenhow could plump."

Again Learoyd rooted up the innocent violets. "Aye, he should see th' bowels o' th' earth an' never naught else. I could take him a mile or two along th' drift, and leave him wi' his candle doused to cry hallelujah, wi' none to hear him and say amen. I was to lead him down the ladderway to th' drift where Jesse Roantree was workin', and why shouldn't he slip on th' ladder, wi' my feet on his fingers till they loosed grip, and I put him down wi' my heel? If I went fust down th' ladder I could click hold on him and chuck him over my head, so as he should go squashin' down the shaft, breakin' his bones at ev'ry timberin', as Bill Appleton did when he was fresh, and hadn't a bone left when he wrought to th' bottom. Niver a blasted leg to walk from Pately. Niver an arm to put round 'Liza Roantree's waist. Niver no more—niver no more."

The thick lips curled back over the yellow teeth, and that flushed face was not pretty to look upon. Mul-

vaney nodded sympathy, and Ortheris, moved by his comrade's passion, brought up the rifle to his shoulder, and searched the hillsides for his quarry, muttering ribaldry about a sparrow, a spout, and a thunder-storm. The
5 voice of the water-course supplied the necessary small-talk till Learoyd picked up his story.

"But it's none so easy to kill a man like yon. When I'd give up my horses to th' lad as took my place, and I was showin' th' preacher th' workin's, shoutin' into his
10 ear across th' clang o' th' pumpin' engines, I saw he was afraid o' naught; and when the lamplight showed his black eyes, I could feel as he was masterin' me again. I were no better nor Blast chained up short and growlin' i' the depths of him while a strange dog went safe past.

15 "'Th'art a coward and a fool,' I said to mysen; an' wrestled i' my mind again' him till, when we come to Garstang's copperhole, I laid hold o' the preacher and lifted him up over my head and held him into the darkest on it. 'Now, lad,' I says, 'it's to be one or t'other on
20 us—thee or me—for 'Liza Roantree. Why, isn't thee afraid for thysen?' I says, for he were still i' my arms as a sack. 'Nay; I'm but afraid for thee, my poor lad, as knows naught,' says he. I set him down on th' edge, an' th' beck run stiller, an' there was no more buzzin' in
25 my head like when th' bee come through th' window o' Jesse's house. 'What dost tha mean?' says I.

"'I've often thought as thou ought to know,' says he, 'but 'twas hard to tell thee. 'Liza Roantree's for neither on us, nor for nobody o' this earth. Doctor War-
30 bottom says—and he knows her, and her mother before her—that she is in a decline, and she cannot live six months longer. He's known it for many a day. Steady, John! Steady!' says he. And that weak little man pulled me further back and set me again' him, and talked

it all over quiet and still, me turnin' a bunch o' candles in my hand, and counting them ower and ower again as I listened. A deal on it were th' regular preachin' talk, but there were a vast lot as made me begin to think as he were more of a man than I'd ever given him credit for, 5 till I were cut as deep for him as I were for mysen.

"Six candles we had, and we crawled and climbed all that day while they lasted, and I said to mysen: ''Liza Roantree hasn't six months to live.' And when we came into th' daylight again we were like dead men to look 10 at, an' Blast come behind us without so much as waggin' his tail. When I saw 'Liza again she looked at me a minute, and says: 'Who's telled tha? For I see tha knows.' And she tried to smile as she kissed me, and I fair broke down. 15

"You see, I was a young chap i' them days, and had seen naught o' life, let alone death, as is allus a-waitin'. She telled me as Doctor Warbottom said as Greenhow air was too keen, and they were goin' to Bradford, to Jesse's brother David, as worked i' a mill, and I mun 20 hold up like a man and a Christian, and she'd pray for me. Well, and they went away, and the preacher that same back end o' th' year were appointed to another circuit, as they call it, and I were left alone on Greenhow Hill.

"I tried, and I tried hard, to stick to th' chapel, but 25 'tweren't th' same thing at all after. I hadn't 'Liza's voice to follow i' th' singin', nor her eyes a-shinin' acrost their heads. And i' th' class-meetings they said as I mun have some experiences to tell, and I hadn't a word to say for mysen. 30

"Blast and me moped a good deal, and happen we didn't behave ourselves ower well, for they dropped us, and wondered however they'd come to take us up. I can't tell how we got through th' time, while i' th' winter I gave up my job and went to Bradford. Old Jesse were at th' door o' th' house, in a long street o' little houses. He'd been sendin' th' children 'way as were clatterin' their clogs in th' causeway, for she were 5 asleep.

"'Is it thee?' he says; 'but you're not to see her. I'll none have her wakened for a nowt like thee. She's goin' fast, and she mun go in peace. Thou'lt never be good for naught i' th' world, and as long as thou lives 10 thou'lt never play the big fiddle. Get away, lad, get away!' So he shut the door softly i' my face.

"Nobody never made Jesse my master, but it seemed to me he was about right, and I went away into the town and knocked up against a recruiting sergeant. The old 15 tales o' th' chapel folk came buzzin' into my head. I was to get away, and this were th' regular road for the likes o' me. I 'listed there and then, took th' Widow's shillin', and had a bunch o' ribbons pinned i' my hat.

"But next day I found my way to David Roantree's 20 door, and Jesse came to open it. Says he: 'Thou's come back again wi' th' devil's colors flyin'—thy true colors, as I always telled thee.'

"But I begged and prayed of him to let me see her nobbut to say good-by, till a woman calls down th' stair-25 way, 'She says John Learoyd's to come up.' Th' old man shifts aside in a flash, and lays his hand on my arm, quite gentle like. 'But thou'lt be quiet, John,' says he, 'for she's rare and weak. Thou wast allus a good lad.'

"Her eyes were alive wi' light, and her hair was thick 30 on the pillow round her, but her cheeks were thin—thin to frighten a man that's strong. 'Nay, father, yo' mayn't say th' devil's colors. Them ribbons is pretty.' An' she held out her hands for th' hat, an' she put all straight as a woman will wi' ribbons. 'Nay, but what they're pretty,' she says. 'Eh, but I'd ha' liked to see thee i' thy red coat, John, for thou wast allus my own lad—my very own lad, and none else.'

"She lifted up her arms, and they came round my neck i' a gentle grip, and they slacked away, and she seemed fainting. 'Now, yo' mun get away, lad,' says Jesse, and I picked up my hat and I came downstairs.

"Th' recruiting sergeant were waitin' for me at th' corner public-house. 'Yo've seen your sweetheart?' says he. 'Yes, I've seen her,' says I. 'Well, we'll have a quart now, and you'll do your best to forget her,' says he, bein' one o' them smart, bustlin' chaps. 'Aye, sergeant,' says I. 'Forget her.' And I've been forgettin' her ever since."

He threw away the wilted clump of white violets as he spoke. Ortheris suddenly rose to his knees, his rifle at his shoulder, and peered across the valley in the clear afternoon light. His chin cuddled the stock, and there was a twitching of the muscles of the right cheek as he sighted. Private Stanley Ortheris was engaged on his business. A speck of white crawled up the water-course.

"See that beggar? Got 'im."

Seven hundred yards away, and a full two hundred down the hillside, the deserter of the Aurangabadis pitched forward, rolled down a red rock, and lay very still, with his face in a clump of the blue gentians, while a big raven flapped out of the pine wood to make investigation.

"That's a clean shot, little man," said Mulvaney.

Learoyd thoughtfully watched the smoke clear away. "Happen there was a lass tewed up wi' him, too," said he. Ortheris did not reply. He was staring across the valley, with the smile of the artist who looks on the completed work. For he saw that it was good.